A hundred years
of
Going to the
Creamery

Going to the Creamery

A hundred years
of
Going to the
Creamery

John A. Quish

A Hundred Years of Going to the Creamery
Published in 2010
by
The Creamery Press
31 Fremont Drive
Bishopstown, County Cork
Ireland.

Contact John A. Quish by e-mail at *creameryjaq@gmail.com*

| ISBN | Paperback | 978-0-9567525-1-2 |
| | Hardback | 978-0-9567525-0-5 |

A limited edition of 150 copies of this book has been printed in hardback

PRINt
IRISH
CLÓBHUAILL
IN ÉIRINN

Design and layout - Bill Power

Printed by Walsh Colour Print, Castleisland, County Kerry.

For my dear wife, Patricia,
daughters Anne and Emma,
and to all those whose daily task was
Going to the Creamery.

Contents

Illustrations

Acknowledgements

This book started when I was working in Russia in the city of Cheliabinsk some 2,500 kilometres east of Moscow, about 1997. During that freezing Russian winter I wrote about some memories of life in the creameries in the 1950s and of farming in the same period. The notes were in the laptop for years and popped up about four years ago and advanced to a finally finished book much to my surprise!

This did not happen without the help of many other persons, friends, and past colleagues and indeed new acquaintances. Special thanks must go to those who read the first partial drafts, my sister Mary Healy, Peter Foynes, Sean Lane and Bill Power who pointed out necessary revisions and redrafting.

I want to say a very special thanks to Bill Power for the final critical editing. His experience, expertise and dedication were central to the final product on which he worked as its 'light-handed' editor.

Special thanks also to Noel O'Shea for his intimate knowledge of the UCC Experimental Creamery and its equipment. Catriona Mulcahy, UCC Archivist, went to a lot of trouble tracing old photographs and lists relating to the opening of the Dairy Science Institute and Experimental Creamery.

Sean Lane, general secretary, Dairy Executives Association and his personal assistant, Sylvia Matthews, let me free with old records on the Irish Creamery Managers Association which were most helpful and useful.

Mary McCarthy-Buckley was always ready to listen and help and first told me about the work being done in Mary Immaculate College in Limerick by Maura Cronin. I went to meet Maura and discovered a wealth of information in the audio and interview project supervised by her. This was written up in a paper titled 'Remembering the Creameries' and which Maura kindly allowed me to quote from in this book.

Finding photos of travelling creameries was like looking for hen's teeth, but John Murphy came up trumps with some really amazing images – even a John Hinde postcard from Cahirciveen. The Dairy Disposal Company (DDC) was something else - the files in the National Archives in Dublin were restricted – special permission must be obtained. However I traced a history of North Clare creameries by Eddie Cotter – whom I worked with in Ennistymon for some months on a Travelling Creamery – a really unique experience. I got to view a copy but had to return it within days and also got pages from a book on West Clare creameries again through John Murphy.

The largest section of the DDC was the Condensed Milk Company, Lansdowne, Limerick, which also included the Newmarket Dairy Company that had its headquarters office in Cork City, just down from the Coliseum corner. Looking for some photographs I travelled to Limerick and met Vincent Gleeson and Pat Falvey. Both were most helpful and Pat gave me some irreplaceable photos of Lansdowne, Knocklong and Tipperary plants from the 1920s and '30s, even though he had only met me that day. Thanks Pat.

Getting photos of Drumcollogher Co-op Creamery Museum was arranged by Seamus Stack and on the day by Ted Bradley, who also scanned documents for me, including probably the only surviving example of the DATI Creamery Manager's Certificate. The Irish Co-operative Organizations Society was very helpful. I was given full access to a box of old photos. Many thanks to Ciara Pelly and DG John Tyrrell.

I finally got some really good photos of the old Dairy Science building at UCC from a booklet on the faculty in 1951, and scanned them. Thanks to Professor E.C. Synnott (retired).

My first cousin, Bertie Hanrahan, read some of the original essays on farming in the 1940s and kept urging me to do more. An avid vintage man, he features in the 90-year-old reaper and binder photos. Bill Power also allowed my to use some of his unique private collection of photographs of Mitchelstown. The Irish Examiner also granted permission to use photographs from their collection.

If I have forgotten anyone, please forgive me - the ould head is not what it used to be! Any and all errors are mine.

Finally, to my dear wife Patricia, who has put up with me for more than fifty years, especially as a bookworm who can wreck a room in ten seconds flat. I am also warned not to start another book – but then there's Russia, Africa, the Ukraine and Kosovo and many photos.... I dedicate this book to her patience and love.

John A. Quish,
September 2010.

Foreword

It was in the city of Ashgabad in Turkmenistan, Central Asia in 1999 that I re-started to put together bits of writing which I had begun in Russia in 1997 and which have now finally ended as A hundred years of Going to the Creamery. My project in Turkmenistan was that of providing a new creamery for the production of pasteurised milk in cartons and manufacturing Gouda type cheese for the city of 500,000 which was financed by Europe Aid.

Remembering the way creameries operated in Ireland in the 1950's and 60's I realised that nobody had written anything about this important aspect of rural social and economic history in a general historical sense I set down a series of articles and kept adding to them. When I finally stopped working in 2007, I seriously put the rest together. This I could not have done without help from many quarters.

There are many excellent individual co-operative creamery histories available in the last few years and these have provided an important account of these enterprises. My approach whether correct or not is to give a picture of what rural life was like in those days and remember the happenings and characters which were applicable to virtually all the creameries from the branch creameries in the rich dairying areas of Munster to the travelling creameries in Clare and West Cork and from buttermaking in the Booleyhouse to the then sophisticated large timber churns of that time period. Telling of the re-emergence of cheesemaking in the 1930's to the training of Creamery Managers and their place in the scheme of things.

Add to this is the key ingredient, the milk suppliers who were all individuals who loved the land and their animals. The Irish have had a special relationship with cattle and milch cows going back many hundreds of years- maybe even thousands. In early Ireland a man's standing in the community was reflected in the number of cows he had and they were equivalent to silver or corn. The huge cattle raids of early Ireland would make the cattle rustling in the Wild West fade into insignificance in their size' figures of 50,000 and 60,000 cattle were common.

Butter and cheese were made in Ireland for thousands of years and butter being the most common of dairy products was made in virtually made in every farm kitchen while cheese was a more sophisticated product requiring more skills and knowledge and thus was confined to the chieftains and 'royal' houses. This trend continued right up to the 18th century with butter being made in every farmhouse and Booley house and the surplus to home use being sold on the various butter markets and in the process creating such great institutions as the world renowned Cork Butter Exchange. The craft of Cheesemaking was lost to the farms and only survived in the 'big houses' being made often by English and Welsh cheesemakers and did not re-emerge commercially until the early 20th century when the Department of Agriculture and Technical Instruction carried out experiments on cheese in Liscarroll Co Cork and later at Ballyhaise in Co Cavan

The invention of the mechanical separator by De Laval in the late 19th century saw the creation of the creamery system and farmers Going to the Creamery for the first time and here we are more than 100 years later and farmers in Newtownsandes are still bringing milk to the creamery on a daily basis.

Going to the creamery was a daily task for farmers in 19 counties in Southern Ireland and in all 6 counties in Northern Ireland in 1956. This was more than just delivering the milk, it was a social event where one met the neighbours and friends, got the news, etc, etc. This was a part of what every farmer was; he learned it from his father, who learned it from his father.

While the discussions of amalgamation were continuing nobody understood the social implications – the sudden stop of a daily event. Every farmer felt a loss, many would not admit it, some were badly affected, particularly bachelor farmers living in isolated areas, so were branch creamery staff, the branch which was alive with the sounds of animals and tractors and arguing and laughter and the hum of the separators were silent.

It was like a death in the family

Listening to some of the audio tapes of Maura Cronin's survey one can pick up the sadness and the desire to talk about the creameries right across the spectrum of all those involved in their daily operation for more than a hundred years.

It is hoped that this book will help to rekindle the memories, the sounds the daily social banter and all other aspects that was Going to the Creamery.

John A Quish,
November 2010.

1
The development of the creameries

Employers of the creamery managers

From ancient times the first Irish settlers Ireland had a close and continuing relationship with the cow and with milk products. There is evidence of cattle keeping in Ireland as far back as 5,500BC when cattle were a distinct part of everyday life. Cattle, especially milch cows, were regarded as a unit of currency and the measure of a person's standing and stature in the community.

Many waves of settlers came from Britain and Europe and later the Celts from as far away as the Danube and Alpine regions. They developed similar lake dwellings to those they knew from their own culture and they dominated and developed Irish culture until the arrival of the Vikings at the end of the eighth century. These Celts brought with them their skills in cattle rearing and herding as well as skills in buttermaking and cheesemaking. These dairy products formed a substantial part of the Irish diet in the far past.

In the ninth and centh centuries, the Vikings settled in communities and in towns and cities mainly

Cuinbattle - cattle raiding in ancient Ireland.

1

on the coastal zone strip. They too consumed dairy produce including fermented milk known as 'bainne clabar,' curds and white cheeses or 'bhanbiath,' similar to the forms of white curds in southern European countries, the South American Quaeso Blanco (Baker's curd cheese and lactic curd cheese) and the Russian and Ukrainian 'Cyr Torag'.

The first references to the export of such products occurs in the 15th century *(O'Shea 1952)* this fact points to the level of buttermaking in Ireland at the time and that it was much more than was required for domestic use. The dairymen of this era were well skilled in buttermaking and in barter trading, with cattle and milch cows in particular raising very high values in silver and in sacks of corn. This period was the start of the English suppression and the confiscation of lands and assignment of land ownership to English settlers and also by suppressing the Catholic religion.

The Penal Laws were introduced in Ireland in the 17th century. These made it illegal for Catholics to purchase land. English landlords rented their lands to tenant farmers and their dairy herds to dairymen, who were mostly Catholic. These dairymen paid rent in agreed amounts of butter per cow. They kept the buttermilk and used it to rear their own pigs – these dairymen were highly skilled and could be regarded the forerunners of the creamery managers.

In or about the early 1630s, butter began to be packed in wooden firkins for export. A firkin was a barrel-type container made from oak or other hardwood. The full size butter barrel carried two hundred-weights (100 cwts = 101.6kg) while the firkin which carried 56 pounds (56lb = 25.45kg) was _ barrel.

Butter markets were held in many towns in Cork, Limerick, Kerry and Tipperary. The largest of these had operated in Cork City since 1722 and even earlier. In 1769 a Committee of Merchants was formally established in Cork and lead the start of the Cork Butter Exchange in 1770 to co-ordinate the grading and export of butter. This Committee resolved 'That we shall ship no butter which shall not be publicly inspected, marked and branded' the basics of the system adopted was the classifying of all butter into a range of qualities, in the beginning there were three and later increased to six. In or about 1830, the symbols/brands used were like these. Being first, second, third, fourth, fifth, sixth.

The quality brands of the Cork Butter Exchange

This farsighted move of a quality led approach was a key to its success and exports of butter to many parts of the world, including North and South America, Spain, India and Australia – a truly amazing operation and a further pointer to the job which later became creamery managers and dairy executives.

'By the close of the 18th century, butter specially packed in Cork for long distance trade to hot climates, had acquired an international reputation. Cork's incomparable expertise in preparing butter for tropical regions was recognised by experts. Only Cork butter was deemed as suitable for re-export to Brazil via Lisbon, the West Indies and North America. This expertise was in the main due to

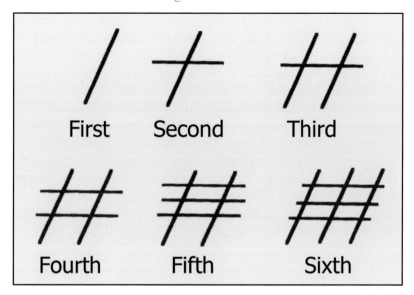

The quality brands of the Cork Butter Exchange.

The Cork Butter Exchange.

the excellence of the Cork coopers and butter packers' *(Rynne 1998)*. This came down to quality butter and quality packaging. In the end, it all transcends to a small number of professional thinking Cork merchants becoming market innovators and the market created by them became the largest of its type in the world.

In the 1820s and '30s, there was a downturn in agricultural production. This occurrence, followed by a rigid 'no change policy' in spite of a requirement in the need for a milder butter saw the stagnation and final closure of the Butter Exchange.

The second half of the 19th century saw the establishment of butter blending factories that purchased fresh and lightly salted butter from farmers. The factories blended, reworked and packaged better quality butter and thus competed with the traditional system of butter trading.

Later in the 1880s, butter manufacture became a centralised factory operation where collected cream was churned into butter. Between 1884 and 1886, farmers in

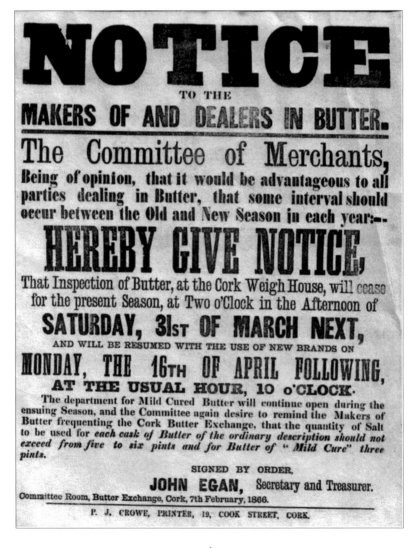

Cork Butter Exchange.

east Limerick and south Tipperary established 'gathered cream' creameries for butter manufacture at Hospital and Galbally, County Limerick and in Golden, County Tipperary. The Hospital creamery was equipped for both cream and milk intake and was established by a Church of Ireland clergyman named Canon Baggot. These were the first of the proprietary creameries established by English owners. *(Foley 1993)*

The first co-operative creamery was established and opened in Dromcollogher, County Limerick, in 1889. The Irish Agricultural Organization Society (IAOS) was founded in 1894 when the number of co-ops had grown to 33. By 1900, there were 171 central creameries and 65 auxiliaries or branchs in operation. Of these only 64 in Munster were co-operatives, the others were owned by individuals, joint stock companies, firms of provision dealers, butter buyers or by the Co-operative Wholesale Society (who had 70 creameries). A number of joint–stock creameries failed because of poor commercial effectiveness. By 1900, the Department of Agriculture and Technical Instruction (DATI) was established with Sir Horace Plunkett as vice-president. DATI aimed to put some structure on the industry which by thenm in addition to the number of co-ops, there was 274 proprietary creameries giving a total of 530.

The Dairy Disposal Company Creamery at Tipperary.

Large buttermaking creamery in the 1950s, location unknown.

Dowdall Brothers' Creamery in Charleville,
one of the proprietary creameries.

Most of the managers of these operations were untrained with the rest itinerant advisers from England. It was clear that there was a need for trained personnel to operate these creameries effectively. In 1896, the National Education Board started a short six-week course for the training of creamery managers at the Munster Institute in Cork and at the Albert Agricultural College in Glasnevin, Dublin.

In 1901, following the setting up of DATI, Sir Horace Plunkett outlined a comprehensive scheme for agricultural education. Consequently, in 1903-'04, a new six-month course for the training of creamery managers was offered at the Albert College, Dublin which covered:

        Chemistry and Physics
        Dairy Farming
        Dairy Bacteriology
        Dairy Engineering
        Dairy Business Methods
        Followed by one-year in-plant training

The Irish Creamery Managers' Association (ICMA) was founded in 1899 and had spread throughout the 32 counties by 1904. The pursuit of a viable certification scheme came into play in 1914 with its own examination. Many of the candidates for the ICMA examinations took the courses in Ballyhaise or the Albert College in preparation for the exam. This continued until the early 1930s, by which time the UCC course was well established.

Sir Horace Plunkett
First Vice-President of the new
Department of Agriculture and
Technical Instruction (DATI)
and also founder of the co-operative
movement IAOS.

In 1911, the course was transferred to Ballyhaise, County Cavan, where it continued until 1916 when it returned to the Royal College of Science in Dublin where it was expanded to three twenty-week terms over two years, which included 'hands-on' training in an operating creamery. The final move to UCC was made in 1924 when the Faculty of Dairy Science was established where it commenced full-scale operations in 1926. A full accountof the dairy faculty is given in chapter three of this book.

Patrick Bolger wrote in '*The Irish Co-operative Movement*' in 1977, that
The Creamery Manager was a key man. A good committee was important, but

Distribution of Creameries by Province, 1906.					
Province	Proprietary	%	Co-operative	%	Total
Munster	365	76.5	112	23.5	477
Ulster	28	14.7	162	85.3	190
Connacht	16	26.2	45	73.8	61
Leinster	20	35.7	36	64.3	56
Ireland	429	54.7	355	45.3	784

the manager's performance determined whether the Society flourished or failed, hence good committees hired and fired until they got the right man, but good managers were not plentiful.

The 530 creameries created as many problems as it desired to solve. The 294 proprietary creameries had only one objective – profit, to buy milk at the lowest price possible, to make butter and sell it at the highest possible price in the shortest possible time. The largest owner of creameries was the CWS of Manchester, in the main established to help the Co-operative consumer with the best quality goods and produce at the lowest possible price. Thus its ideology was not in keeping with the Irish movement.

To make matters worse, it built twelve new creameries and ended up owning over 90 creameries, many too close to other creameries to make economic sense. In the end, remoteness from their HQ and poor management commitment added to milk price difficulties saw their demise; it took until about 1912 to see the last of the CWS creameries sold. At the same time other proprietary creameries were being taken over by co-operative societies in a fairly constant pattern. In 1902 Castletown, Effin, Templebreedin and Cappamore were acquired from the Maypole Company, Rathneveen, Donoughmore and Berrings from J & J Lonsdale and Millowen in County Cork from a Mr Ellis.

Patrick Bolger continues:
Many proprietors of private creameries were gombeen-type merchants who had an innate propensity to adulteration and sharp practice. Many of them mixed margarine with their butter: others cheated their suppliers over gallonage or butter test. These peccadilloes did not always go undetected and sometimes were fined serious sums. The gombeen's answer in almost every case was further exploitation of the milk supplier to recoup lost profits, either in a straightforward reduction in the milk price or by other underhand dealings.

Improvement in butter quality

From the beginning, the creameries gained their footing because of the invention of the mechanical cream separator. This was followed by the mechanisation of the butter churn and improvement of quality through better working of the butter.

Much butter was still made on the farms in the 1920s. Some was of very good quality especially when it was made by farmer's wives or daughters, who had been trained by the instructors in butter-making. However, most was of poor quality and not good enough to satisfy the higher demands of the new purchasers who could choose from the world's finest dairy produce. Basically the writing was on the wall for farm-produced butter. The introduction of surprise butter inspections were carried out by the dairy produce inspectors who helped raise the standards of butter manufacture and marketing. This continued to later form the basis for the Read Cup Competition, which was presented each year at the Royal Dublin Society Spring Show in Ballsbridge.

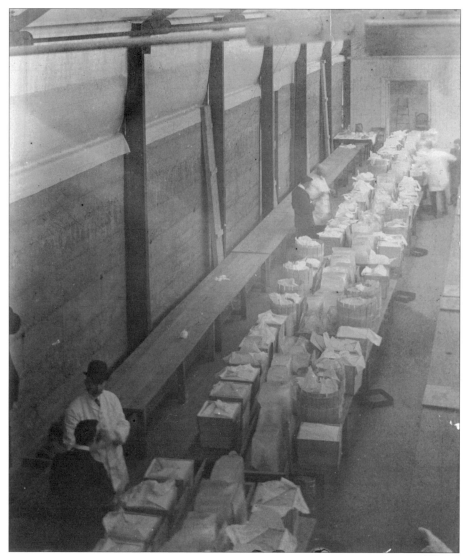

Surprise Butter inspections, final judging at the RDS Spring Show.

Compared to Denmark, where the marketing was highly organised, the Irish industry was very lax. One attempt was initiated by the IAOS which helped form the Irish Associated Creameries Ltd in 1928. Some 80% of the co-op creameries joined the new organisation and agreed to deliver most of their butter to it. However, the twenty per cent outside the IAC Ltd included some of the most important and progressive creameries who continued to manufacture butter on their own. The individualism of creamery managers was very much in evidence where many claimed they could get better prices on their own initiative. After a very short life, the Irish Associated Creameries came to an end in 1930.

The Reid Cup when it was won by Ballyclough Co-op in 1966. Included in the picture
are P.J. Power (left of cup), Denis Murphy (behind cup) and John Myers.
(Bill Power Collection)

While co-operative creameries may not have prompted suppliers to be remark-
ably loyal or scrupulous about the quality of the milk which they delivered, it was
generally better than that delivered to the private operators. Better, cleaner, fresher
milk resulted in fewer losses and in a butter which was of better quality and could
command a higher price.

This higher quality was a direct result of the pressure from the IAOS and the
efforts of the ICMA to improve technology and business efficiency. Indeed, many
of the managers were outstanding pioneers of agricultural efficiency and
development in their own districts. Most of the busiest managers nevertheless found
time to give invaluable service to the IAOS through its national and provincial
committees.

Dr Maura Cronin wrote in her contribution to *Ireland's Heritage - Remembering
the Creameries* (2005), said that

> *The creamery manager was central to the success and identity of the creamery.
> Indeed, one creamery history, that of Drangan in south Tipperary, had its
> chapters arranged by manager : 'The William Murray period,' 'The Ned Hall
> Period,' 'The Jim Blackwell Period,' 'The Pat Sugrue Period' – four managers*

11

spanning over half a century. The neighbouring (and rival) creamery at Mullinahone had only just twelve managers over a ninety-year period, the last 68 years being dominated by four managers [Drangan Centenary Committee 1997 Foley 1993] *along with the priest, teacher and doctor, the creamery manager was at the top of the local social pyramid, the Limerick Rural survey of the early 1960s describing him as being of exceptionally high status.*

'Farmers believe that it is necessary to be on good terms with him because he has great economic power. The creamery provides a limited number of jobs for farmers' sons. So many farmers' sons compete for the small number of jobs that they are valued far more than they are worth. It is a common illusion among farmers that such jobs can only be got by currying favour with the manager. Most of the farmer's earnings came from the creamery, and there is a definite fear that anyone who is not a friend of the manager will get small returns for his produce. (Newman 1964)

From north Kerry came a story, possibly not totally accurate, but illustrating the same myth of the managers omnipotence.

Three farmers were talking about the best way to get a good return at the creamery. The first fellow said: 'I feed the cows raw potatoes: that brings up the milk yield'. The second said: 'No, you'd be better off to boil the spuds first, and then give them to the cows'. The third said: 'Not at all. I find you're better off with raw spuds, but it isn't to the cows you give them. Give them to the manager'.

But neither the survey nor the myths accurately capture the complex relationship between the manager and suppliers. Power and status there was, frequently embodied in the creamery manager's house, equal in standing to that of the parish priest. But such status was dependant on the manager's success in running the creamery.

The manager in those days, the creamery manager, it was policy that if he was a successful man and got on with the farmers he stayed, and managers in creameries as far as the farmers were concerned were probably there to stay if they were successful and getting on with the farmers. So, in the time period that I remember the creamery, there would have been three or possibly four managers over quite a long time period.'

Many managers went far beyond the call of duty by quietly stepping in to advance money to suppliers who were in economic difficulty, squaring the debt when times improved. Nor was this linked with any undue personal prosperity on the manger's part as he was very much second-fiddle to the more powerful members of the creamery committee, on whom he depended for increases in salary. As one former manager from County Clare explained:

It might have been a well held job in public eyes, but it was never a well paid job. No, because there is no money in the farming industry, only, so we were never a well paid group, we were just adequate at best. And while we might have the perception of honour and glory, that was as far as it went. People certainly

*would have asked us our opinion on various things and in that sense people
looked up to a few key figures in the parish, whereas they now tend to form their
own opinion.*

A major problem in these early days was the non-availability of milk in the winter
time to keep the creameries going and it was slow to change. In the main it was due
to the calving time of the cows. It never did fully change but stretched out to some
ten or eleven months. The only milk production within the farming sector that fully
adjusted, being the liquid milk sector which had about fifty per cent of the herd
calving early and the other fifty per cent at a later period and thus having a full 365
days milking which is necessary for large liquid milk markets in Dublin and Cork.
This was done through a contract system and supervised by the Dublin and Cork
district milk boards, established in 1936 under the Dairy Produce Act, and giving
the suppliers a premium per gallon of milk which helped the extra cost of a dual
herd.

The Condensed Milk Company of Ireland (CMC) was one of the larger
proprietary creamery groups. It was founded by Thomas Cleeve and others in 1889
to manufacture condensed milk and butter. It later became manufacturer of the
famous Cleeves Toffee at Lansdowne in Limerick. By 1900, the CMC had 2,000
employees and 3,000 farmers with a chain of smaller creameries and factories
throughout Munster. Its exports reached most parts of the British Empire and in all
owned some 114 of the privately owned creameries.

Following the departure of the CWS, other private creameries continued to be
taken over by co-ops or closed due to commercial difficulties leaving only two main
groups pf proprietary creameries operating – the Condensed Milk Company of
Lansdowne and the Newmarket Dairy Company with headquarters in Cork.

The period from 1913 to 1920 were good years for the co-operative creameries.
Despite the difficulties and shortage of supplies and raw materials during World
War I, farming prosperity continued. Good prices were being paid for milk and by
late 1919 the creameries were the mainstay of income for most farmers' survival. In
addition to economic difficulties following the end of the First World War, in 1920
the War of Independence was raging, resulting in a series of reprisal raids against
co-operative creameries by British Forces who believed that they harboured
nationalist sympathisers. Starting on 9 April 1920 with an attack on Rearcross
Creamery, more than fifty other reprisals were carried out on co-ops. At least 35 of
these attacks were on creameries, others being farming supply stores, thereby
resulting in serious property damage and disruption of operation with a consequent
loss of close to £1 million.

By 1922, Ireland had entered a period of severe economic depression. The
number of creameries had begun to outpace the available milk supply resulting in
a virtual price war. By 1926, there were some 580 central and auxiliary creameries
in operation of which 400 were co-ops. Of the other 180 proprietary creameries, 114
were controlled by the CMC, which had by this time taken over the Newmarket
Dairy Company. The CMC was a progressive company with new products and a

Truck fleet at Lansdown Dairies.

large UK wholesale grocer as a shareholder *(Lovell & Christmas)*.

In 1924, the Dairy Produce Act was introduced. This was a very important and comprehensive piece of legislation relating to the production and manufacture of dairy products. All creameries were required to be registered and adhere to strict standards in buildings and equipment and the employment of properly trained staff, including the qualification of creamery managers.

By the end of 1926, the trade war reached its climax and the outlook for co-op dairying was very poor. The price war continued and seriously damaged the financial base of many co-ops. Even the powerful CMC was unable to sustain the withstand the difficulties.

Probably the most significant event at this time was the appointment of Dr Henry Kennedy as secretary of the IAOS. A giant of a man in stature and in intellect, and a committed believer in the co-operative movement, Kennedy and the

IAOS prompted the then young Department of Agriculture to negotiate with the Condensed Milk Company with a view to purchase their creameries and manufacturing plants.

Dairy Disposal Company

The Government and the CMC reached agreement on purchase and, in 1927, the Government, through Patrick Hogan, Minister for Agriculture, set up a state-sponsored body, the Dairy Disposal Company Ltd, to acquire and manage the creameries involved until arrangements could be made for their integration into the co-operative system. The first acquisitions were the Condensed Milk Company of Lansdowne, Limerick, plants in Knocklong and Tipperary, and branch creameries. Uneconomic branches were closed as were others who were deemed to be too close to co-ops. Others were transferred to co-operative ownership.

In the period up to 1931, the DDC purchased 110 proprietary creameries. Of these, 79 were closed, 44 were transferred to co-op ownership, and the remaining 47 were retained by the DDC. The DDC also took over 17 co-op creameries, of which four were closed, 13 were retained and four new creamerieswere built. Toames Co-op was transferred to the DDC in 1932, and two years later, eleven others were simultaneously transferred including the well known Kerry creameries in Ballymacelligott, and Rathmore in 1935. The DDC as an organisation was run by civil servants and creamery managers. Although many creameries were 'saved'

Lansdowne complex in 2010. The factory is now owned by Kerry Foods.

through takeover by DDC, there was also concerns that it could be accused of 'empire building'

In 1928, the Creamery Act introduced a system of licensing which enabled the Minister for Agriculture to control the establishment of new creameries, which effectively prevented the setting up of creameries in unsuitable locations. In 1930, a co-operative creamery was established n West Clare, the central creamery being in Kilrush with a branch at Cooraclare. Due to difficulties with calf mortality this co-op got into financial difficulties and through the efforts of Bishop Fogarty, the DDC took it over. Subsequently, 16 other branches were built and the whole west Clare area was developed into one of the largest buttermaking units in Munster. The creamery manager was Mick Lane. In 1933, the North Clare Creameries was established at Ennistymon by the DDC.

In the years 1927 to '29, about twelve new central co-op creameries and 18 independent auxiliary creameries were established to serve areas in the Midlands, West and other underdeveloped areas.

The Dairy Disposal Company Ltd had been established in 1927 as an interim solution to help reorganise the dairy industry and to ensure it settled easily into co-operative control. Many years passed, however, without this change taking place

The Lansdowne complex from across the Shannon in the 1920s.

and the DDC seemed to become more and more a permanent entity and an empire building operation of some civil servants and creamery managers who controlled it. The biggest problem this semi-state body had was that in every year it was expected to pay its way and provide its own capital for any expansion. In this way, like many other semi-state bodies at the time, it was willing but unable to undertake the risks and entrepreneurial creativity of changes and plant development which would have given it a true developmental and industry leadership role, including the specialist training for creamery managers.

In view of this difficulty, the management just did its job well but showed little initiative, like many other semi-states of the same period (CIE, the rail and bus company, would be a good example of this especially when it dismantled tracks and sold off land which could have had huge development potential in the future).

The DDC began to show a considerable resistance to yield either its assets or its territories to any co-op takeover. The stagnation and at times a face-off between the co-ops, IAOS and the DDC continued despite continuing pressure on the Minister for Agriculture and his Department in 1937, and despite 'promises, promises'. No real success was secured until the purchase of DDC creameries in the Newmarket area of County Cork by the Newmarket Co-operative Creameries in 1944.

Roller dried skim milk powder in the 1950s.

While this may have appeared to be the beginning of the end for the DDC the final road was long and hard with continuing clinging to power and staff were particularly reluctant to give up the job status they held as direct employees of the department of Agriculture with all the perks of civil servants and little help from government or its department - it took another 30 years to break the DDC.

Cheese

John McCarthy in his historical paper to a Cheese Symposium in 1992, cited four periods of commercial production which are related to the timescale of this book. Starting in 1901, experiments were carried out at Liscarroll which continued until 1906. By 1912, the Department of Agriculture and Technical Instruction had given its blessing to cheese manufacture and by 1915, some twenty factories were making Cheddar and Caerphilly. Exports began about 1913 and grew year on year to 14,500 tons by1919, with some 200 factories producing cheese, mainly cheddar. Disaster occurred in 1920 with the affect of price de-regulation at the end of 1919 resulting in a drop by 1921 to 1,500 tons.

The period from 1922-'32 saw a virtual standstill with exports less than twenty tons by 1932 mainly due to prices and market difficulties and so contributed little. The period from 1933 to 1948. saw Mitchelstown entering the cheese business and in addition to natural cheese obtained an exclusive licence to manufacture processed cheese for the next 16 years. During this period, Mitchelstown became the biggest co-op in Ireland and had a virtual monopoly in cheese, both natural and processed, resulting in the complete elimination of imports in 1941.

The period 1949-'61 marked the formation of the Golden Vale Group which comprised a consortium of twelve cheese-producing creameries processing and marketing their whole output of cheese. Since the Mitchelstown monopoly on processed had ended in 1952, Golden Vale initiated its own processed cheese brands. The ensuing competition was good for the industry and for natural cheese consumption. This period saw many changes in technical aspects of cheese manufacture with production reaching 5,000 tonnes by 1960 and per capita cheese consumption going from 0.95 kg to 1.22kg and the introduction of rindless cheese.

During the 1960s, very significant expansion took place, with some seven new cheese factories being commissioned. By 1970, cheese production reached 27,700 tonnes. Four other additional manufacturing facilities were created in the 1970s. Production reaching 48,900 tonnes in 1980. Further expansion brought production to 78,500 tonnes by 1990, of which more than 72,000 tonnes were exported – a truly amazing performance form less than 1,000 tonnes in 1950.

Liquid Milk

For many living in and growing up in rowing up in Ireland during the years of World War II, the daily supply of milk came from a local milkman. In my home place, Mick Farrell, better known as 'Mick the Milkman,' had a few cows in some fields near the railway station and delivered milk from a twenty-gallon churn with a tap at the end. From the tap he filled a covered pail with a spout – about four to five gallons – and when he came to the door he poured out the milk into a pint measure and emptied it directly into my mother's jug. This was the same in all towns and cities from the start of urban settlements up to the time of the Milk and Dairies Act in 1935, which regulated the quality of milk offered for sale for human consumption.

In larger cities the milk was bought by the milk vendors from an approved source, Limerick - Lansdowne, Cork (the University College Creamery). but in Dublin a number of large farms started their own milk processing plants – Hughes Brothers dairy in 1926; Merville Dairy (owned by the Craigue family) at about the same time, a smaller dairy near Leopardstown called Tel-El-Kebir (TEK) and the

A Merville horse drawn milk dray.

oldest of all, Lucan Diaries in Islandbridge, which gave 300 gallons to the city during the visit of Queen Victoria in 1900. Pasteurised milk in glass bottles was produced in Dublin from the mid-1930s.

Pasteurisation at this time was not compulsory but expected in view of the widespread TB. The supply of bottled milk in smaller towns did not occur until the late 1940s through companies such as Snowcream and Drogheda & Dundalk Dairies. The establishment of the Dublin and Cork Milk Boards in 1936 brought further control and better times to liquid milk producers during World War II, with Martin J. Mulally being chairman until 1975, at which time Bill Twomey took over until the boards were abolished in 1994 - probably another poor decision for farmers.

Cork Milk Producers (CMP) was established in Cork and Clona Dairies at Clonakilty. With the subsequent amalgamation of the co-ops into larger units, there was an eventual reorganisation of the liquid milk sector, with Glanbia currently holding the lion's share of processing, but marketing under a range of logos.

A proud profession

Thus the progression of the industry from small beginnings in the last years of the 19th century to the modern and technically sophisticated sector of the 21st century has provided continuing employment for creamery managers, who themselves were the driving force and innovators of progress. Their training and experience had equipped them for many roles, not just in Ireland but in the food and dairy industries of many countries.

Indeed, in my own small way, I have contributed to that spread of Irish know-how by teaching cheesemaking and commissioning dairy processing plants in more than forty countries since 1990. Many important innovations in cheese cultures and in dairy chemistry and many other sectors were made by Irish dairy and food scientists in the research centres such as Moorepark and at University College, Cork. These have kept Ireland at the pinnacle of the dairy industry worldwide.

Indeed, I recall an occasion in the mid-1960s when I was doing some post graduate studies at Penn State University, USA. I was travelling west of Chicago with a technical executive of the Creamery Package Company (H.L. Mitten). He was telling me of a visit he had been on to New Zealand and of meeting another Irishman who was the senior dairy adviser to the New Zealand government. I asked him to name the man, it transpired that he had been a friend of my father and had worked with him as a young creamery manager in Mitchelstown in the 1930s.

The industry in Ireland, including research and development, has provided and continues to provide constant employment for almost 1,000 creamery managers and dairy executives At least another 200 in co-operative agricultural stores and many hundreds in the dairy, food science and technology operations in the UK, US, European Union and many other countries of the world.

Cork Butter Museum

Cork Butter Museum is the only privately-owned museum which focussed on butter, its origins, cultural and social importance and its economic benefits for Ireland. The museum is situated on the actual site of the world renowned Cork Butter Exchange which exported world quality butter from 1772 to the 1920s and under its Committee of Merchants introduced the first food quality designation in the then world.

The museum has a range of exhibits including 1,000 year old 'bog butter,' and utensils and items used in butter making from the earliest times. The extent of the markets covered in the 'heydays' of the Cork Butter Exchange are shown. More modern methods and successes of the Irish dairy Board since 1961 are exhibited in explained through film, video and slide projection.

The museum is beside the refurbished 'Firkin Crane' which was a part of the butter exchange and is now a dance theatre and studio. It is also close to Shandon church. The exhibition in the museum covers two floors and is both educational and interesting in a sector of Irish food which had its beginnings more than 5,000 years ago and continues to be one of our most important exports. The museum was founded in 1997 and operates under a board of trustees. Peter Foynes is their director and curator who arranges a special guided tour for specialist groups. The museum operates from seven days a week opening time 10am to 5pm, between March and September. Specialised educational material is available for schools.

The train at Mitchelstown stating, facing for Glanworth and Fermoy. The engine is a Mc-
Donnell 4-4-0 of class D19.

(Bill Power Collection)

Looking down the line to Ballindangan, Glanworth and Fermoy.
The goods-shed on the right and the signal box on left.

(Bill Power Collection)

2

A country education

The early days - farming in the 1940s

The lure of the relation's farm, the steam train journey and the mystery of milking. Although I had lived in a town, I had always been close to farming. Both my dad and mam's families were all farming and so if we visited the 'relations' - it was to a farm and since both were from large families, there were many farms. My mother had a very close sister on a large farm in Ballyhooly which was about twelve miles away, but we went to Glanworth by train and my aunt met us at the station in the pony and trap.

The train journey, for a boy of eight, was an adventure in itself. The walk to the railway station in Mitchelstown was only 15 minutes - but I couldn't wait. This station was a full stop and there were so many things going on that I was goggle-eyed! The ticket office was part of a long station house built of cut limestone, a long single story building with the station master's office and then his residence. In front was a wide platform with a three foot drop to the oily shiny tracks. While mum was getting the tickets I noticed the rack of different little hard cardboard tickets of various colours in racks, when the clerk pulled out one for mum it made a click, he passed it out - where's mine - Oh! You're free!

As we went out there was a loud blast of a train whistle and the train swept up to the platform with belch of steam, a draft of hot air and that never to be forgotten oily, steamy ,sooty smell so characteristic of steam trains and a screech of metal to metal as the brakes went on. Doors swung open, passengers came out, porters were busy, then with a clank the heavy chain was dropped from the engine and it chuffed up to the turntable which took the engine and coal wagon, whistles sounded, men shouted, pulled levers and pushed hard and slowly the huge engine turned around and chuffed on an outside track to a huge water tank, where with a cloud of steam it filled up with water and reversed back to the train for the journey.

By this time we were sitting in the carriage and soon were on our way rushing through the countryside through level crossings with their closed gates, under road bridges with a roar and through rocky cuttings with a rush, one short stop at Ballindangan, where my mother's home was, and we were off again to shortly cross the high steel bridge at Ballykinley over the Funshion river - it was some 80 feet over the river - but to a boy of eight it seemed 800! We glided into Glanworth station with a spurt of steam and a screech of brakes. Mum let down the window with the leather strap and opened the door. We stepped out and found Auntie Joan waiting with my cousin, Bertie, in the pony and trap for the 3 mile drive to Rahard and the farm.

The farm

Even in these early days during the war years, this was a big farm, with a long thatched farmhouse and a large yard with a variety of outhouses giving a courtyard effect. In a further yard was a haybarn, the cow byre and further again a very large shed housing a huge steam engine and a thresher. The whole place was a hive of adventure. Shortly after a feast of tea and white country bread with currants in it - 'just hot from the bastible,' said auntie Joan 'put plenty of butter on it' - and we did!

'Run out now and let ye help to bring in the cows,' as my mum and herself sat down, of course what they really wanted was to get us out of the way so that both of them could have a chat about things we were not allowed to hear. Since the farm was big and, depending on where the cows were grazing, bringing them in for milking was done walking or using a horse and cart I enjoyed the longer runs sitting with my legs dangling over the front edge of the cart, Bertie behind me and Uncle Mick driving the big dark horse.

My uncle was always a great lover of horses and kept a lovely grey working

Molly O'Brien of Bally-organ, County Limerick, hand milking in the 1950s. This is not the Molly O'Brien mentioned in the text.

(Bill Power Collection)

stallion called 'Price Arthur' - he was treated like a king and had his own special house. A large section of the farm was woodland and scrub covering some 40-50 acres, this was the 'wood,' and I well remember 30-40 wild, unhandled horses and foals galloping free - man! this was really close to Gene Autry or Hopalong Cassidy cowboy country - it was especially thrilling when the men were trying to catch some for training and selling. Yes! They did use a lasso! It was of course from this stock that came the horse pulling the cart - and Prince Arthur was the daddy of them all - literally!

Running beside the cart were the dogs. These were sheep dogs of dubious breed but very good with cows and cattle. When we reached the field where the cows were, uncle would shout to the dogs 'gwaan! bring 'em in Rover' - a black dog with a white forehead. Off raced the dogs and even before they reached the cows, they (the cows) had turned, stopped grazing and made for the gate - they knew the time. Sometimes one of the cows would be a bit slow and Rover would nip at her ankle to remind her. The cows rambled along the track back to the cowhouse. Sometimes the bull was with the cows. On those occasions there was no fear that myself or Bertie would venture down from the cart. In his 'stately presence' even the dogs were wary and gave him a wide berth.

Uncle Mick had about forty milking cows (a large herd for those years) and the cowhouse would only take 10-15 at a time. Waiting in the yard the cows knew their turn and would enter the shed and move to their byre. These byres were made of two upright planks, one fixed upright and the other fixed with a bolt at the bottom and movable on the top to form a wider gap. The cow's head went through the gap and by slotting over the movable section into an upright position, and fixing it in place with a pin, the cow was unable to withdraw her head until released after milking.

In front of their heads was a concrete channel into which hay or a special mix of rolled oats and barley was put for the cows to eat while milking. Sometimes mangles or turnips were used and these had to be chopped. This was done in a special chopper called a pulper. This was worked with handle like a wringer, the blade had special grooved sections which sliced long thin ribbons from the roots - and was made by Pierce of Wexford !

At that time, all the milking was done by hand and there were about four or five milking including my aunt and uncle. Hand milking was a learned skill. The cow's four teats were used to empty the udder or 'dug' as it was often called at a fair - 'Jasus Jack that wan (cow) has a great dug, she's a good milker.' Incidentally, in later years it was not uncommon to use similar terms to describe the endowment of certain young country lasses in the Ballrooms of Romance - 'a heavy milker' - Nudge! Nudge! Two teats were milked at a time, usually diagonally - the skill of milking was -'squeeze - draw - ease - cycle' rhythmically applied to the two teats in sequence - or was it 'ease - draw - squeeze'. Ah! Heck! It's a long time ago.

It was my first time in the milking shed, so close I was a bit wary, and the cows were much bigger than they seemed in the fields. After a short while, I got used to them as they seemed so peaceful munching away at their feed - it was funny watching their mouths chewing away in a kind of a flat circle. Auntie Joan tied a scarf around her head and with a clean bucket in her hand, she went between two cows, my cousin Bertie handed her a small three-legged milking stool and she sat down and put the bucket under the cow's udder. I was watching fascinated and suddenly I got a squirt of hot milk into the face. I spluttered and Auntie Joan, Uncle Mick and Bertie breaking their sides laughing at me - then I laughed too! That is until the next cow lifted her tail and lets go a stream of shite, the spatters were way worse than the milk! As the milk hit the side of the bucket, it hummed like a tune for a few minutes until the bottom was covered. The cow took about ten minutes to milk and the bucket was emptied into a high twenty-gallon milk churn through a cheesecloth strainer.

While most cows were docile during milking there were always the rogues, who for no apparent reason would kick out and send milker, bucket and stool flying! This lady got the 'spancil' for a week or so to straighten her out. The 'spancil' was a short length of rope or 'sugan' which tied the cow's hind legs together while milking, so that she could not kick.

When the milking was finished, the cows were left out to a field near the house, so that they would be close for the morning milking. If my uncle had a new milker or a temporary one he would always make sure that the cows were fully milked or 'stripped,' as the 'strippings' were the richest part of the milk. Sometimes if the cows were nervous or uneasy, due to rough handling or other reason, they would hold back part of the milk and if so, it was always the 'strippings' or the richest part of the milk. This was why my uncle often said 'you should sing to the cow while milking and you'll have a higher test!' He hadn't a note in his head!

The churn with the evening's milk was now put on a raised platform in a part of the yard well exposed to the elements, so that the milk was kept as cool as possible. The lid was checked to make sure the cats would not prise it off, with the buckets washed and the cowhouse swept, it was time for tea.

So the mystery of milking was solved for me. A few short years after that my uncle bought a milking machine, I remember it was a GVB of New Zealand, imported by Drinagh Co-op and hand-milking faded into the past.

Footnote.

In recent years I again saw hand milking, in Zambia, where 100 cows were milked by natives . They milked on the grug, without a stool. I asked the farmer, an Englishman, why he did not have a milking machine. He told me that spares were impossible to get but there were plenty of natives! This Englishman farmed 4,000 acres - 'services rendered to the Queen in India' and had wheat, milk and Polo horses! Where have we heard that before.

Cutting the corn with the reaper and binder

I spent most of my school summer holidays in Rahard. My cousin Bertie and I were more like brothers than cousins (and still are! Eh! lad!) Both interested in machines, we spent many happy years tinkering with peddle cars of our own design and hours building mechanical marvels with Meccano sets, an addition to the collection from Santy at Christmas was a must! (Why! Oh why did I not keep my Dinkey Armstrong Siddenly, it's worth a fortune now!)

It all started with the bastard! Sorry! The bastard file. I was about twelve or 13 and the hay-cutting was frantic in the fine weather, anyway the knives on the mowing machine needed sharpening and Uncle Mick was short-handed. Now the knife (even today) was made up of sections, these were hard steel plates with an angular front which had two sharp edges. These were riveted to a long flat steel plate which slided between cast teeth and driven with a reciprocating arm at high speed. After a time they got blunt and that's where I came in. I was a dinger to edge the sections with the 'bastard'.

One summer there was great excitement. Uncle Mick had bought a tractor! It was a Fordson with the standard orangy colour and iron front wheels and flat steel wheels at the back which had holes all over. I learned later these were for bolting on 'spade lugs' to give better grip.

A picture of contentment.

1940s scene in 2009.

These photos were taken in 2009 cutting oats with a rebuilt McCormack- Deering binder with my cousin Bertie on the binder near Rathcormac. The machine is nearly 90 years old.

Before using the tractor, Uncle Mick and Paddy Nash (his cousin, a gifted mechanic) decided to put in a new clutch. Bertie and I were riveted to the barn where the operation was carried out. 'We'll have to split her,' says Paddy, as he started to remove bolts in front of the back wheels. They build up a stack of heavy timbers under the front part and when all the bolts were removed, they pulled and tapped and cursed and swore and pulled and swore until slowly a gap appeared. Another stack was built under the rear axle and finally the tractor was in two halves. We were enthralled! While serious work continued on the repair, we were kept out. 'You two stay out of here,' ordered Paddy.

'That shaggin' yoke could slip and kill ye'. So we went off and played in the engine shed, climbing on to the huge steam engine and turning the big steering wheel with it's handle, the massive iron rear wheels were all of six feet in diameter, and the shining four foot fly-wheel, used for driving the thresher. Then we would move to the big thresher and 'check it out' for the harvest' - we knew every inch of it and how it worked!

With the barn out of bounds we would annoy Mike Keating, as he was getting the horse drawn McCormick reaper and binder ready for the harvest, which was only a few weeks away. This was complicated machine, all driven from a wide metal wheel under the centre, with a smaller outrigger wheel on the cutting side. The whole unit was worked from the main wheel through a series of chains and gears.

In the front was the cutting knife which was made up of triangular sections riveted to a flat steel rod. This slid into a slot between a series of cast-iron pointed 'fingers,' the width of cut was the length of the knife, being about four or five feet. When the wheat was cut, it was guided with a big slow turning reel and fell onto a guide that turned the cut wheat sideways and on to a flat canvas. This canvas ran between two rollers and had wooden laths riveted on about every foot, and thus pulled the wheat back in from the knives about three to four feet. Here it met two other similar canvas rollers mounted at about a 60 degree angle, each moving upwards in the middle and which carried the wheat up and on to a series of packing arms against an end gate. At a pre-arranged interval, an automatic knotter would place a length of heavy twine around the bundle, knot it, cut the twine and eject the now formed sheaf of corn. Biders were temperamental bastards and 'Murphy's Law' applied all the time.

After our lunch, Uncle Mick, with a big grin on his face says, 'come on over to the barn, we have something to show ye'. We had, at this stage forgotten about the tractor, so off we went excited. When they opened the doors, we could not believe our eyes. There was the Fordson ready to go with beautiful new rubber front and rear wheels. Paddy and uncle busied themselves with oil cans and petrol cans and setting fuel valves. Then Paddy says, 'Right let's try her'. He caught the starting handle and gave a few pulls. Putt! Silence. He adjusted a lever slightly, another pull - a few more putts! A few more putt-putt-putts and with Paddy juggling the throttle lever, a throaty roar and away she went. After warming it up for a few minutes, Paddy and Uncle Mick got on to the seat and the platform and off they went up the yard and we chasing after them.

Fordson tractor similar to the one rebuilt.

That year they converted the reaper and binder to be pulled with the Fordson and we were all there for the first field test. While we watched, fascinated at the way Paddy manoeuvred the tractor at the end of each run, we were soon put to work building 'stooks' with the sheaves. Later that year, Bertie and I got our first tries at steering the tractor and stood beside Mike Keating as he cut a field of barley. Coming to the end of a cut, he watched until the knife cleared the barley and then put on full left lock straightened up and did a full circle to position the knives at right angles to where he came out of the crop - it looked very simple but required practice and skill to perfect it.

Coming to the end of the cut there was only a small square of the crop standing and Uncle Mick watched, with his shotgun cocked, and the red setter stood alert. Suddenly, a rabbit or a big dark hare would break from the crop and race for the ditch. Uncle Milk or the setter never moved as the sheep dogs took off in full flight, the setter moved facing a spot where the binder had just passed. Uncle raised the gun to his shoulder - with a rush, a rustle and a frantic beating of wings, a fine cock pheasant rose from the spot - five - ten - 15 feet. Bang! Bang! We would have pheasant soon for Sunday dinner.

Another aspect of these unforgettable times, was the afternoon 'tea' in the field. The women would appear with basket and an old sweet gallon. The tractor and binder stopped. We would all sit on a sheaf with our backs to a 'stook' as the white enamel mugs were passed out and filled with hot sweet tea from the gallon. Then the hot heavily-buttered slices of fresh 'bastible' cake, well dotted with currants and raisins, was handed out. Nothing tasted so good. There was always a special flavour from the tea, the hot fresh cake dripping with butter was, well, you guess. It had to be experienced.

Uncle Mick was the man in the neighbourhood with the machines and so with his own work done he would contract cutting, threshing etc., in the surrounding farms. During the summers following, I drove the Fordson, and with Cornie Henchion on the binder we did our tour. Getting in and out narrow gates and bohereens (little country lanes) doing our own running repairs, and eating in the fields or the local farmhouse was a wonderful experience, with practice I could get in any gate two inches wider than the binder!

Summer recreation – and scares!

During the years when I drove the tractor at Rahard I was lucky to be getting a few pounds from uncle Mick and so I traded in my old black bicycle for a flashy green sports one. On Sunday evenings I would head off the cinema either in Fermoy or Mitchelstown to see the derring do's of James Cagney, Alan Ladd, or John Wayne and cycle the five or six miles back to the farm in the still dusk long summer evenings. One Sunday going to Mitchelstown just outside Glanworth I met this other lad also cycling to the' pictures', I knew him to see and that he worked for a farmer and had heard - God between us and all harm - that he wasn't 'the full shilling 'beaganin as a bheabhr,' mhar a der to.

Anyway I was glad of the company and off we went .himself showing off pedalling mad in front of me because I had the fancy sports bike. Now there's a long slope down to Ballykinley bridge across the Funshion river and half way down there's a cottage. They kept a few goats. These goats grazed the 'long acre' and two were standing in the middle of the road.

By this time there was a bit of a race and I was gaining, spotting the goats I swung over to the right side and tore past them, expecting yer man to come up beside me ,when I hear 'Oh! Jasus! I'm shaggin kilt'. I brake hard and skidding sideways to a stop look back to see yer man flying through the air and the bike another. Thinking to gain on me he went to go between the two goats - they were tied together at the necks!! -That was the end of his Alan Ladd!

Another Sunday night I went to Fermoy to see John Wayne in the 'Flying Tigers,' waiting for the programme to begin and listening to Ruby Murray singing 'Softly, Softly'. Over the speakers there was a huge ah! no! from the audience when the manager announced, 'sorry but the wrong film was sent. I'm afraid you're going to see 'The House of the Vampires'. He was afraid! - jez I hated these films, and me having to cycle home to Ballyhooly! Anyway I stayed, was scared out of my wits and headed for home. It was still fairly bright and a full moon was rising so I figured I'd make it back in a half hour - the back wheel was nearly flat! Ten minutes to pump it up. The clouds started to appear and it got dark quickly, my only light was a hand held torch and with me trying to break all records, I could not hold it.

Passing a small old graveyard the sweat was flowing and every bush and tree was hoarding a ghost or at least a vampire bat! By this time I'm trying very hard to rationalise the situation and that there's only about 3 more miles, but by now it's pitch black! Suddenly! I hear a rattle of chains and then another -the hair on the back of my neck must be standing straight up! I can't see a thing ,I drag out the torch and switch it on --only to see two big red eyes just to my left, I nearly fell of the bike when a friendly voice said 'Hello! a bit dark to-night isn't it'. 'Oh ! Ah! Yes It is indeed'. It was a local farmer leading a bull with a long chain on to his nose ring.

Anyway this sorted me out and I felt a bit of a fool and mad at myself for being such an eegit! By this time it was fairly late and Auntie Joan was always trying to find out what time I got home .So this night I quickly put the bike in the shed and pushed open the kitchen door - there's a metallic crash as the metal fire shovel ,placed against the door by Auntie Joan falls on the concrete floor, I'm so mad with all that happened I gave it a kick into the big kitchen where it clattered along the floor and woke everybody. I went to bed and thought - 'well now she'll know what time I came in'!

Aunt Kate - a gifted buttermaker

I never really knew what relation she was to my mother but to me and my sisters she was always Aunt Kate. Since we passed her house going to Auntie Joan we always 'dropped in 'for a visit.

Two things stick in my mind from this place - there was a big flock of white geese with a right cross bastard of a gander and the Aunt Kate was a gifted buttermaker. She could make superb farmhouse butter in three different types, the traditional highly coloured fermented (ripened) cream butter, the mild creamy salted and the mild creamy unsalted.

This was quite a range of butter types for the 1940s and was in the main due to the shortages created by the Second World War in Europe. Normally the traditional farmer's butter was her product, the others being made by the creamery, but now rationed. The milk used was from the home farm, the 20 or so cows being mainly the traditional Shorthorns with 'a few handy Kerrys' - 'to bring up the thest' (sic) - (Since milk was paid for on butterfat only ,this practice was common). Aunt Kate knew the best cows in the herd and selected the milk from these for her butter.

Her dairy was a small room about eight-feet by twelve-feet off the yard and it was always kept locked, it was quite a thrill and a privilege to be invited to visit it. I was always fascinated and very curious as to what everything was for and I'm sure that I nearly drove her to the limit with question after question. Aunt Kate at this time was certainly in her sixties in the mid-forties - she would try to get rid of me saying 'can't you run across to the orchard and get an nice red apple, that's a good boy' - I wouldn't move, not because I didn't want an apple - I was afraid of the bloody gander!

Anyway, in the dairy was a long heavy wooden table, on which were two or three very wide shallow tinned metal basins, these were filled to the top with cream. There was a butter churn with a turning handle, mounted on a heavy wooden stand. It was like a large Guinness porter-barrel with a large elliptical opening that had a metal lid with a rubber seal and held in place with a hand screw. It also had a sight glass through which you could see the milk. The most intriguing item to me was the milk separator. This also was worked with a turning handle and was bolted to a raised concrete stand in the centre of the floor. It had a large metal bowl on the top and lower down two spouts, one over the other but at different angles. When the handle was turned, and it was very hard to start, it started to hum and was a 'beautiful noise'. The day I first saw Aunt Kate separating, I stood there rooted and enthralled. She first turned the handle slowly and then faster until the hum was at

Cream skimming and ripening dish.

the right pitch. (Many years later I learned that the handle had to be turned 90 times per minute and some separators would ring a bell if the speed dropped off).

At this stage, she would call the farm boy to turn the handle and would pour warm water into the bowl on the top. When there was a gallon or so of water in the bowl she opened up a tap and the water flowed into the top of the separator, as the water flowed the note of the hum changed and within a minute it flowed out the lower spout on to the floor. As the last of the water left the bowl, she poured in the warm milk from a bucket on the floor and now the note changed again, and I saw the farm-boy sweating from the pressure of the turning - but he dare not stop!

Aunt Kate was watching the lower spout carefully and suddenly the colour changed, the water became white and then milky, she placed a clean bucket under the spout and turned to me saying 'this is skim milk, the young calves love it'. She picked up an enamel mug and let some flow in, handed it to me - 'taste it' I did and spat it out – I did not like it and felt sorry for the calves.

This is the product we now buy as non-fat milk for slimmers, and pay more for! She then put a bowl under the higher spout and shortly a drip and a steady flow of

Hand cranked separator
similar to Aunt Kates
[CBM]

lovely cream poured into the bowl - a taste of this I did not refuse at all. In about 40-50 minutes there was about two gallons of cream which was covered with muslin and left to cool, and the poor farm-boy was fit to drop! The washing of the separator was a big job, since there were a large number of very small parts and if one was lost the separator would not work - so nobody but Aunt Kate did this job.

Aunt Kate only made butter about twice a month as it took this time to collect enough cream and for it to have fully 'ripened'. The ripening took place in large shallow dishes made of tinned steel, these were filled with the cream and covered with a muslin cloth and left to ripen. At this point, the cream was very thick and was slightly sour to taste, the cream was poured into the timber churn until it was nearly half full, the metal lid was put on and the screw tightened to seal the opening. Then the churn was turned around and around with the handle and the cream slopped around and around the churn. After about thirty minutes she stopped and pressed a little metal button on the top of the churn and there was a hiss of gas escaping,

Butter churn similar to
Aunt Kate's

then she continued churning. After about another 15 minutes, she stopped and looking at the little sight glass, pointed and said 'look, see the specks,' and yes, there were little specks of yellow sticking to the inside of the glass. 'The cream is breaking now,' says Aunt Kate and instead of a slopping sound from the churn there is a splash! splash! as the solid pieces of butter fall from top to bottom of the churn as it turned.

She opened the churn and let me see the little lumps of butter floating on the white buttermilk. She poured the buttermilk out while holding back the butter. This was when I had my first taste of real buttermilk - it really was lovely! She rinsed the butter granules with cold water a few times in the churn before taking out the beautiful yellow butter on to the clean table. Here she beat and beat it and mixed it with hand butter spades and explained that this was to get all the loose water out and was called 'working'. The butter was then wrapped in parchment and put to cool.

Before we went she got two little timber blocks and put some butter on top, then she pressed the butter and smoothed the top and turning the blocks over on to a plate. Two little lumps of butter fell from the hollow blocks, shaped like cows.

'There now,' says Aunt Kate, 'won't that be nice for the tea'. And it was.

It was buttermakers like Aunt Kate who were the source of the butter which was delivered for many years to the Butter Exchange at the Firkin Crane in Cork City. They made their butter and filled a firkin and then buried it in a section of bog to mature for a few months so that they had a full pony cart for the long haul to Cork.

Garden Fete

One summer, I can't put a date on it, we all went off to garden fete at Annesgrove the home of the Annesley family. This was a beautiful stately country house set in magnificent gardens which were the main attraction. It was probably a charity function. As well as the attraction of the gardens, there were many side shows for both adults and children alike, with swinging boats and rings and air rifle competition, which to my great joy my father won with a score of 39 out of a possible 40. He got a lovely vase as a prize, to the joy of my mum. After this he took me to see the field where the pleasure flights were being given, I could hardly contain myself with excitement when I saw the plane putter in over the low fence and land, turn around and taxi over to stop only ten or 15 feet away. I had never been so close to a real aeroplane before but had already built models. Anyway I was warned that I was too young and that the price was far too dear at 15 shillings for 15 minutes! But I was happy even to watch. The aeroplane could carry three and the pilot. How I envied him. The aeroplane had a single wing that the people stepped on to get in. It also had three tail fins on the back wing. There was a long queue waiting and when the doors were closed a man went to the front, and on a signal from the pilot, gave the polished timber propeller a deft pull. With a roar and a puff of smoke the engine started. After a few minutes the plane taxied out to the far end and turned into the wind. The engine roared louder and the plane moved faster and faster. The tail rose and it lifted gracefully into the sunny summer sky.

Then my dad woke me back to reality and it was time to go home! But we never know how things in our young days affect us in our sub-conscious. I have been an aircraft 'nut' ever since childhood and many years later learned to fly and still do. I have what the well known aviation writer 'Richard Bach' called 'a gift of wings,' and for me nothing can compare to flying a small Piper Cub over beautiful Irish countryside on a calm summer evening at the fantastic speed of fifty miles per hour, with the side doors open at 1,500 feet!!

The Master Wheelwright and carpenter

About a mile from Uncle Mick's, on the road to Castletownroche, lived Jim Cotter. The house stood on the 'v' of two roads and had a big dark-coloured workshop in the yard at the back. Jim was a tall slim rough faced man with a quick smile - but the hands were the thing, they were big strong and yet refined – and gifted.

Miles Messenger aircraft as seen in Annsgrove

Jim could make timber do anything for him. I was no hurler, being from a traditional Gaelic football area, but the best hurley I ever had, Jim Cotter made for me. To watch him make a timber wheel for a horse's cart was a never-to-be-forgotten experience. I'm not sure of the actual sequence or the types of timber but he would start with a large block of timber and with a small sharp hand-axe would shape it into a perfect cylinder, maybe ten or twelve inches in diameter. This would be the wheel hub. He would then measure and mark very carefully, using a big flat pencil, constantly over his right ear.

He treated his tools like a surgeon, taking out the set of chisels, laying them on the long bench and carefully inspecting each one and honing to a razor edge on his unwrapped oil stone. The standard horse's cart in those days had two large wheels about four feet in diameter, made up of four or more segments, each with two spokes which joined the rim to the hub. No nails or bolts were used in the best wheels and they would last - for ever!

With his chisels and wooden mallet the wood would fly, moving the chisels with deft accurate movements and short sharp strikes of the mallet, he would stop, look and chip, move to the next position and repeat .then taking from the over bench rack a spokeshave he would finish the edges in his own particular way - part of a work of art was ready. It was a beauty. The trade of Christ Himself.

The rim segments had been part prepared the day before and after steaming in a tray to make pliable Jim forced them firmly but gently into a special timber jig to set overnight. Carefully removing them, he laid them out on the floor forming a perfect circle though slightly overlapping. Again the pencil and rule appeared and with deft movements laid out the joint overlaps and the exact positioning of the spokes. There was no rush, no figuring, no inadequacy, he knew. That quiet confidence of the master who knew his craft, his skill - his life.

Each rim segment was worked and shaped with the same care and skill, the chisels would flash and the chips would fly and the mortises for the spokes would magically appear. Finally the spokes were fashioned and the fits checked (the modern engineering term being 'interference fit'). Jim started the assembly first taking the hub and fitting the spokes, driving them fully home with deft blows of the timber mallet. Then taking each segment he would fit the spokes and trim the joint overlaps. With the wheel fully assembled Jim would do the final trimming and dowel each rim segment overlap. The final two operations were a joint one between himself and Tom the blacksmith down the road, these were the making and fitting

Cart wheel being
assembled.

of the steel rim and the fitting of the cast metal centre hub. On one such occasion Bertie and I went with Jim to the forge, He had a light springy cart and it was pulled by a sprightly piebald colt, which looked and was as jumpy as a race horse. Off we went with the two wheels in the back and Jim laughing we tore down the road at a rate of knots to the forge.

Tom the blacksmith was big , strong, smiling broadly as we pulled up and wiping a sooty arm across his sweating forehead says to Jim 'Jaas, Cotter you're a mad hoor the way you drive that crazy friggin' colt – you brought the wheels I see'. 'That shagger won't do anything I won't let him,' laughed Jim .The wheels were laid out on the forge floor and Tom coming over ran a tape deftly around the outside of each wheel ,turned to Jim and smiling said, 'still the best Cotter, Chrisht! There's not an eighth-of-an-inch between them'. Jim guffowed loudly and replied, 'yerra com'on now Casey, you'll be looking for me to buy you a pint for all that plamasing. Where's the fekkin' rims'. 'Ah! don't be getting yer tail in a twisht

Jimmin, sure they're all ready and chamfered only for riveting and then into the fire,' replied Tom, as he pulled two circular lengths of steel strap from a corner and laid them on the floor.

Deftly measuring each, he marked the chamfered ends, and taking them to a big vice, positioned the first, and with a big geared hand-drill deftly bored the rivet holes in them. Before positioning the second rim, he tossed two one-inch rivets into the flat forge fire and turning to Bertie and me said, 'come on now you two and earn ye're dinner, pump up that fire'. Tom pointed to a long leaver about five feet high. It was the handle of a huge bellows and as we pulled it down, it forced air in under the grate just like the fire machine in the kitchen, only much stronger. In a short time the fire was glowing white hot and Tom, returning from drilling the second rim, raked hot fire over the rivets and within minutes they too were glowing from the intense heat of the white hot coals.

Raking the fire, Tom picked out one glowing rivet with a long handled pincers and taking it over to the rim in the vice, he skilfully manoeuvred the red hot rivet into the drilled holes on the rim, then gripping the rim at the joint with the pincers he removed the rim from the vice. Placing the riveted rim over the big anvil, he deftly flattened the head of the softened rivet with five or six blows of a heavy hammer. Tom repeated the exercise for the second rim and when finished they placed them on top of the wheels. 'Jays !Casey yer after makin a proper bollix of them,' shouted Jim, (with a wink to Tom that we did not see).

Bertie and I look at each other with concern for Tom, but then the two of them roared laughing and to the pair of us beckoned to the big forge fire. 'Come on! More bellows work for you two,' as he raked out the fire, spreading it out to the full size of the grate which was some five feet square and putting on fresh coals from a stack in the corner. As we pumped, Jim and himself picked up a rim and laid it on the fire which was now glowing red all over and raked some coal until the rim was covered. 'Work away now lads,' says Tom, 'an' I'll tell ye what we're at'. 'Ye thought that the rim was too small, well that's true, but not entirely, when we heat the rim in the fire it will expand with the heat and get bigger. Then Jim and myself will lift it on to the wheel which is now in the tray. You'll see it will just fit, and as it cools it will squeeze very tightly on to the wheel'. As the work continued we watched fascinated as the first rim cooled and tightened on to the wheel. The strength of the squeeze as the rim cooled was amazing. We would hear the spoke-joints tightening with little cracking noises and the smell of the burning on the timber under the hot rim. Our day had been great and the engineering lesson we had, though not realised at the time, was never forgotten

With the rims in place, the last item was the cast hub bearing which was fitted in similar fashion. Purchased complete from the foundry, it was a cast cylinder machined on the inside to fit the axle which was about one inch in diameter. The outside was slightly tapered with two or three raised ribs to lock it in place and a lip on the outside edge of the hub. The hub had been drilled out by Jim to fit the nose of the taper, as with the rims, the bearings were put in the fire and again we pumped the bellows until they were glowing red hot. The wheels lay flat on the floor as Tom recovered the first bearing with a long tongs which fitted around the bearing just under the lip.

He put it into position and with a light tap from a heavy hammer, it stood smoking. Jim took a steel sledge hammer and placed it on top of the red hot bearing. Tom picked up another sledge and with a rain of strong strokes on the first sledge drove the smoking bearing home to its lip. Repeating the job on the second wheel the task was finished. 'Jas Tom that's thirsty work com'on an' I'll buy you a pint - the lads will mind the place for a half hour,' - and we did.

These wheels were the standard used for all horse drawn carts for many decades. They were used on the butter roads to carry firkins of butter from Kerry and West Cork to the Butter Exchange in Shandon and to carry beef, pork, potatoes and corn back to the far towns of Kerry and West Cork.

Threshing by steam engine

Uncle Mick inherited the threshing set from his father. Part of the youthful magic of that farm was the 'Engine Shed' which housed the steam engine - a big black and brass Marshall - and the thresher with it's myriad of belts and pulleys. Sunday evenings were often spent with Bertie and I giving each other 'spins' on the shakers - although we were expressedly forbidden from doing so.

Come July and August, the corn harvest was in full swing. While the wheat, oats and barley was being cut with a reaper and binder, Uncle Mick and his cousin, Mick Keating, were busy getting the engine and thresher ready for the season. On the engine the fire box would be cleaned out, all the bearings oiled, and the stuffing boxes readied. The steering chains were checked, the smoke box cleaned and the fire tubes brushed. Although we were filthy from head to toe, Bertie and myself could not be dragged away from 'helping' and we were 'as happy as pigs in shit'.

All chores done, the water tank was filled and the fire lit. As the fire gained strength, the smoke sprang from the stack with that unique oily smell so reminiscent of steam engines. Slowly the pressure gauge on the boiler flickered at first and climbed tantalisingly to 80 p.s.i. Uncle Mick opened the steam valve and let steam to the engine and with a sudden swoooch the huge four foot flywheel started to turn.

Then with a deft movement of the clutch lever, he engaged the travel gears and the mighty engine trundled out of the engine shed. Stopping in the wide yard, she sat there spinning away beautifully, the flying weights on the centrifugal governor glinting in the summer sunlight. Then all the belts were checked on the thresher and the drum and concave inspected. I can well remember one year changing all the old bronze bearings for new roller ones - a major job.

The first threshing was at home and the thresher was towed into position with the engine and the levelling started. Wheels were sunk into trenches or jacked up with timber planks. The jack was a box rack jack with very low gearing and high lifting capacity. Next the delicate 'lining up' of the engine to ensure a correct line and

This is a recent photo of the actual engine referred to in the text – now restored and working

'true running' position for the long driving belt. Otherwise it could (and would) fly off at full speed and likely take the head of someone. All was ready late in the evening, all set for an early start the following day. The silhouettes of the machines and the high ricks of wheat stood out in dark relief against the setting autumn sun.

Bright and early the engine was fired up and brought up to pressure. Shortly the neighbours and their workmen arrived to help. Meanwhile the farmhouse kitchen was a hive of activity, with every available pot in fires, stoves and Primus stoves, filled with 'spuds,' hairy bacon and cabbage for the dinner. The cows were milked at 6am and wonder of wonders, Bertie and myself were dispatched with the milk to the creamery at 7.30 with the grey pony.

That morning, afraid of missing anything, that pony was persuaded to move smartly down the road with the milk. We got to the creamery early and were in the first four. The manager, Mr Murphy, in his white coat joked with us as to our milk being sour, but knew of the threshing and let us go quickly, collecting ten pounds of butter along the way. On our way through the village we collected the 'parcel' from Grindle's corner pub, and drove home quickly.

We were just in time as we ran up to the back haggard, the big engine flywheel started to turn, driving the long belt. As the speed built up, the thresher became alive with all the screens and blowers operating and the straw shakers oscillating. As threshing speed was reached, there was a new sound - the characteristic hum from the threshing drum, as it spun inside the concave, waiting to do its job.

With everything set, Cornie Henchion on top was the feeder, he shouts, 'Right lads! Ready? - keep 'em coming now'! With a deft flick, he took a sheaf, cut the twine with his razor sharp cobbler's knife and fed it into the drum following with a constant flow of sheaves across the width of the drum. As the sheaf hit the drum the tone changed again with an 'neauauau... shhhh'! The note of the engine changed also feeling the load, with an almost imperceptible slowing and a quick pick-up settled down.

An early Marshall Thresher in full flight.

Very quickly the threshed straw fell out from the shakers and the first hiss of grain whizzed into the jute sacks. Within minutes the whole operation settled down to orderly confusion. One group fed sheaves to the top of the thresher, another cleared the straw from the shakers and built a rick of straw. The third group tended the bags, sewed the tops as they filled with a large bag needle and shook them in neat rows for transport by the co-op truck which would collect them later.

Uncle Mick watched everything. Mick Keating busied himself keeping water and fuel to the steam engine and deft squirts of lube oil from the long spouted oil can on to shafts and connecting rods. The whole atmosphere was humming - it would seem, in harmony with the engine and thresher. The early slagging and joking being replaced with hard slogging, as the workload increased and then the competition element arrived, with side bets on everything from tossing a sheaf to how long to fill a bag - to what time we stop for dinner !.

Slowly, the first rick of sheaves got smaller and equally across the haggard the rick of straw was now ten to twelve feet high. Bertie and I were used as 'gofors' - and were now told 'tell the kitchen we'll be right for dinner in half an hour'. Off we chased down to the house where another hive of activity was ongoing. The smell of bacon and cabbage wafted tantalisingly before we even got to the door, where the

A typical threshing scene reminiscent of the 1930s to the 50s.

big chunks of steaming cooked bacon was being sliced ready for the dinner and the big black cast-iron pots were still boiling the 'spuds' on the fire. 'Tell them we're all ready here,' says Auntie Joan, and off up the yard with us. From half-way up you could not see the scene but you could hear it, only now the sound was a rising and lowering hum, the pitch changing as each sheaf of corn was enveloped by the fast spinning drum - a beautiful noise.

As the final sheaves were swallowed by the thresher, the first wave of men moved down to a well needed dinner. They were seated around the big white enamelled table with a small mountain of flowery spuds in the centre, big jugs of milk, plates of creamery butter and Aunt Kate's farmer's butter with the higher yellow colour. While this group was eating, the last of the grain ran into the bags and the last of the straw piked to the top of the rick now 15 -18 feet high.

Mick Keating then shut the steam and let the engine and thresher slow to a stop - the silence was deafening - after a constant din of men and machines and now, but for the periodic release of steam pressure from the engine, there was quiet. The fire was kept up, and the steam pressure held for the re-start in an hour.

With the first serving are now finished, several of the more active individuals kicked football in the front field, with the less active having a game of pitch and toss at the corner of the barn. The heavy gamblers usually played pontoon on an up-turned butter box.

Everybody was quickly brought back to reality as the shrill note of the engine whistle rent the air. All trooped back to their own jobs as with a wooch and a whooo the engine speeded up and the thresher reached full speed. Shortly after dinner the creamery lorry arrived for the first load of sacks. These were quickly loaded and off they went to the grain depot. By this time the rick of sheaves was dwindling and the new straw rick was 15 feet high.

The full sacks were again ready for the lorry. It was just about half past four when with a 'neigahh,' the last of the sheaves were fed into the drum and quickly swallowed. Finally, the last of the straw fell from the shakers and the last hiss of the wheat into the bags. The steam was shut off the engine. Slowly the thresher slowed to a stop. You could hear the silence, save for a hiss of steam and the cracks of the contracting metal.

With all the wheat finished, the screens would have to be changed for the oats on the following day, but now everybody gathered around and waited sitting on bags while Uncle Mick tapped the half-tierce of porter. In those times, Guinness was sold in two-size timber casks, one of which was the smaller half tierce, holding 16 gallons. Mick had a brass tap specially for the job. It had a long tapered end and a flat nose to drive it into the wooden spigot. While Mick Keating held the tap Uncle Mick, with a fast clout of the wooden mallet, drove home the tap without loosing a drop! A cheer went up from the crowd as the tasty black porter was poured serenely into a large white enamel jug, forming a lovely creamy head in the process. As all lined up, their glass, cup or mug was filled to the top with fresh lovely Guinness – God bless you Arthur!

A great and memorable day.

Cowboys at Kingston Castle

Mitchelstown Castle, the enormous home of the Earls of Kingston, was looted and burned by the Republicans in the Civil War in 1922. Most of the building was taken away by the monks of Mount Melleray in County Waterford, who ised it to build a new monastery in the 1930s. What was left of its ruins, in our childhood, were a gulch, an Indian camp, an army fort and many other things as we played cowboys and Indians, the sheriff and the James gang, or just hunted there in our summer holidays. There were so many places to hide and jump and chase, it was 'magic'.

The ruins were large (it wsas the biggest house in Ireland) and although on one side it was level where the main entrance had been, there was a sheer drop of some fifty feet at the other site. One Christmas, one of the older boys in the town had a close call when he fell while trying to get some holly, so we were very wary and knew the dangers. We used to go to the castle on a Saturday, via the square at Kingston College, and in the main gates of the old demesne which by then had been divided up by the Land Commission. Its 6.5 mile long walls, ten feet high, enclosed 1,300 acres. Inside the gate was an old slaughter house, which we quickly passed because of the smell! Down through McEniry's land we came to the twig yard, a very important source of ' ghaoulogs ' which were the 'Y' shaped handle for our 'catapults' - the spring in this red barked timber was super. On the right of the 'twig yard was the old entrance to the castle stables which wound up the escarpment on top of which the castle stood. At this time overgrown, it was another magic play ground and led right into the old stable yard which was still standing. Of course, our childhood imagination conjured up all sorts of creepy adventures, from ghosts to secret passages leading to the treasure.

Another path led down from the castle to the caste lake. This was a favourite place for us on summer evenings. It must have been a really magnificent feature during its heyday. It was man made, lined with paving bricks and had a wide grassy

Kingston Castle gates with the milk powder plant on the castle site.
(Bill Power Collection)

bank. As far as I remember, it was 200 yards long by 50 yards wide (less or more I'm not sure). At the time we frequented it, the remnants of the boat house still stood near where the lake was fed by the Gradoge river, and overflowed at the far end back again. As Bill Power has so often described in his books, the lake was a really beautiful piece of engineering and one which should have been kept as a feature of the town's history. Sadly, until the 1980s when a new treatment plant was built, it was used as an effluent lagoon for storing waste from the creamery farm and the milk powder factory. It was unique in the country. As a feature of the demesne, it could have been an important amenity to Mitchelstown, especially with the loss of so many other local buildings such as Galtee Castle and Bowen's Court near Kildorrery.

Another happy playground was equally unique and of particular significance to the town is the ice house (also referred to by Bill Power). Not far from the lake, it looked like a small hill in the corner of a field. On closer inspection, there was a small entrance on to a shelf and a brick lined roof covered with clay. Inside, at the end of a short passage, the building dropped some fifteen feet - the whole round structure was some forty feet in diameter. This was the 'fridge' for the castle and was layered with ice during the winter and used to store meat, butter, cheese and other delacies for most of the year.

These important artifacts belong to our heritage as do the Gun Powder Mills in Ballincollig and the unique planned town of Mitchelstown itself. In recent times I rediscovered the ice house because it is now beside the new Mitchelstown by-pass.

The tree campaign and the cheese boxes, and turf

A friend of my father's, Billy Casey, was manager of the co-op tree cutting campaign. One summer in the late 40s, he took me on a tour with one of the felling gangs. It was on a large estate taken over by the Land Commission and prior to dividing the land to new farmers much of the mature trees were sold as commercial timber. This was probably to defray some of the expense of the purchase from the absent owner, usually in England, and thus enable easier payments for the new lessee. I had never seen big trees felled before. In the days before chainsaws, it was hard work with an axe first and then a crosscut saw. In the hot summer day the sweat poured off the men, when the cut was nearly through there would be a yell of Treee! and all would retire a safe distance. I could never figure out how they knew which way the tree would fall, but these were professionals and could place it exactly as required for easy loading onto the lorries.

On one large estate we visited, there was the big house empty but still with huge character. The keys were available and it was an experience to walk from room to room to see the grandeur still apparent on the ornate ceilings and expensive wallpaper. As one wandered through the house, you could not but imagine the splendour of the heydays of those once magnificent houses and the strange lives of those who lived in them. Then into the Commer van for the drive home, on the way as I watched the speedometer we did 60m.p.h. My first time ever traveling at that speed!

I was told that these trees would end up as cheese boxes for the 5lb blocks of Galtee cheese and that I could see them being made on the following day. So I arrived at the saw mill which was situated in the yard of an old corn mill at Bank Place in Mitchelstown, which in my younger days was used as a cheese store. The logs arrived and were piled in lots to season. The first operation was a big circular saw which cut the tree trunks into boards then re-cut them to the required length. The various special saws were set to give the exact sizes of boards for the sides and the ends. The last section was the nailing which had automatic nailers that were fascinating to watch and were the very latest equipment at that time. As the boxes were finished they were neatly stacked for transport to the cheese factory.

Turf

A few years earlier during the Second World War period, or as it was known in Ireland, 'the Emergency,' there was a severe shortage of fuel. All the creamery boilers had to rely on turf. This was marked by a decision by the then manager of Mitchelstown Cfreameries, Eamon Roche, to cut turf on bogs on the Galtee mountains and stockpile it at the creamery farm. What was interesting about this was that the transport was done by the creamery trucks which had been converted to run on 'producer gas' with the gas producers mounted just behind the cab.

One summer Saturday, my father and some of his friends went to a mountain bog in the Galtee Mountains to cut turf for the winter. They all cycled and I was perched on a special seat mounted on the cross bar of his bike. It was a warm day and the crack was flying as they cut out the sods of wet turf with a special spade called a 'slean,' as they piled on the side of the cut out bog they were piled on their ends in little cones to let the wind through to dry them. I had this job. At first it was fun but later just plain hard work. The break for the tea and sandwiches was very welcome. While the men sat and talked of GAA and greyhounds, I explored, but was warned of any water pools, as they could have been cut out and full of water and very deep. There had been some accidents where people had been drowned.

Anyway by late evening, we were all set to go home and got all our gear packed. On the way home there was great talk of the Sunday ahead as one of my father's friends, Cal McCarthy, had just finished building a new house and was moving in then. As we were going to be there I was very excited, and suddenly I'm screaming as my foot got caught in the front wheel spokes. There was consternation as my father struggled to stop and remove my foot which was bleeding and swelling quickly. I was wrapped up with a towel and we travelled the last mile in record time to Mitchelstown to Doctor Fitzgerald's house. After a quick examination for broken bones, the foot was bandaged and I got an injection which was worse than the damage and I was ordered off to bed.

On the Sunday I was collected to go to the new house by car and soon forgot about the leg - but I still have the marks to show.

Army manoeuvres and 'The Queen Mary'

Another weekend around the same time is brought to mind as I write. I cannot put a year exactly but it must have been 1942, which was the year of the largest Irish army manoeuvres ever held in the country. There was intense activity around the Fermoy and Kilworth areas and at home all the Local Defence Force (LDF) and the Local Security Force (LSF) were all on alert. Some time lat on a Sunday morning, my mother and father were at the front door talking to a friend of theirs who was a member of the LSF and a colleague of my dad's. Of course I was there in the street with them, it was a lovely sunny day. I remember the LSF armband on his arm. Suddenly, there was a loud engine noise and then we were all out at the edge of the footpath staring unbelieving as an army aeroplane came thundering up the centre of the main street in Mitchelstown, only some fifty feet over the road. As it flashed past, we could actually see the pilot. Then it was gone as quickly as it came. Later in the day, the same aircraft swooped down in the large square and off again. Afterwards ,I was sure that the plane was involved in the manoeuvres and probably flew out from Fermoy aerodrome. I recently discovered that it was probably a Westland Lysander observation plane. One sad aspect of those manoeuvres was that during the manoeuvres along the river Blackwater in Fermoy, two soldiers were drowned.

Later that same Sunday, Cal, who was one of the other creamery managers working with my father, (and who had recently built a new house) took us to see the 'Queen Mary'. This was the local nickname given to the building which was the main cheese factory in Mitchelstown. We walked down Lower Cork Street and turned left into Clonmel road, by Russell's big shop and then passed Russell's cinema where a few years later I watched Gene Autrey, Hopalong Cassidy and Tom Mix fight it out with the 'bad guys ' or the Indians. The big building housing the cheese factory was the newest of the large complex and about ten years old at that time. It had a row of black funnel-like ventilating outlets on the roof ridge and it was from this, that it got the name 'Queen Mary' after the then queen of the Cunard Line, which called frequently at Cobh.

We went in and the smell hit us – sweet and sour and a bit sickly. Cal was explaining everything but of course I and Cal's boys, John and Tommy, were chasing around the multiplicity of cheese vats and pipes – a 'magic 'place for boys.

Clonmel road in the 1940's, Russell's cinema was at the far left.

(Bill Power Collection)

Row upon row of 500 gallon vats were lined up ready for the Monday. As we walked on through the different sections and finally into the huge cheese store, with shelves of cheese maturing, Cal produced a testing tool from his pocket. Going to a shelf, he pushed the tool into the side of a cheese, twisted it and out came a round sample for us to taste, which was lovely. Little did I think at that time that I would spend the rest of my life involved in cheese, milk and other dairy and food products and that my first introduction to large scale cheese making would be in the 'Queen Mary'.

Christmas sobriety for 'Mossie'

Needless to mention Christmas time was rife with stories, one trying hard to 'besht' the last one. This one, though short, is really worth relating. Mick at the time ran the family butcher's shop in a large County Cork town and coming up to Christmas was only able to kill and ready the next day's meat in the late evening. In those years, each butcher had a bit of land outside the town where he kept animals he bought and where he had his slaughter house just beside a 'bohreen,' going up to a couple of cottages.

This was the common practice in the 1950s. These were very basic sheds with galvanised sheeting for the sides and roof, with a concrete floor. The sides came only part of the way at the bottom, leaving 15 to 18 inches of a gap at the bottom. There was a good reason for this, as when the animals were 'gutted,' the smell was fairly 'pongy,' so with the bottom open the wind would blow away the smell – well nearly. Anyway and anyhow, on the evening in question Mick was inside the slaughter house finishing off half a dozen sheep for the following day, working by Tilley lamp. He was almost finished about 9 o'clock of a fine cool December night. Who was coming up the lane but Mossie Flynn. He was, as they used to say, 'mouldy-maggoty drunk' after twelve or 14 pints of porter, an' he singing away with the hands hanging, a mixture of *Noreen Bawn* and the *Rose of Tralee* and neither in key. Mick saw all this as he glanced out of the window. He smiled at the spectacle, of yer man staggering over and back on the lane and he in rearing form. The singing stopped and Mick peeped out only to see Mossie making for the gate in front of him and over to the back wall of the slaughter house, while at the same time struggling with the belt of his trousers! 'Jas,' says Mick to himself, 'he's short-taken for a 'shite' and with a few grunts and groans the next thing, he could not but see yer man's white backside under the gap at the bottom of the walls.

'Chrisht! I'll sober this hoor up now,' chuckles Mick, and he turning around and reaching to the centre of the floor, picked up a full sheep's guts and slid it out under yer man's arse! Well as is often the case, Mossie finished his job and stood up and turned to have a look at his handywork, and froze! As he saw the heap of guts in the light shining under the shed, felt himself, tore up his trousers, was fully sobered instantly as he ran out the gate screaming, 'Oh! God, Jases! Holy Chrisht! The fuckin' drink, I've shite me guts'. He was sober until February!

Mitchelstown creamery managers and their wives at a function Mitchelstown 1956/57.

Front row (seated) William Wallace, Michael Higgins, Pat Dowling, J.J. Lynch. Mrs Dowling, W.D. Hayes, Liam Casey, Michael Ellard.
Mid row Billy O'Rourke, not known, Pat Quish, Mrs Mary Quish, Denis J. Broderick, Niall O'Keeffe, Mrs Emer O'Keeffe, Mrs Pat Dowling, Mrs F. Cotter, Mrs JJ Lynch, Mrs M. Higgins, Mrs M. Ellard, Mrs P. O'Donoghue, Paddy O'Donoghue, Mrs W.D. Hayes, Mrs W. Casey, T. Neville, P.A. Roche.
Back Row: not known, P. Clancy, Mrs J. Casey, John Casey, Eamon O'Brien, Florence Cotter, Tom O'Brien, John A. Quish, Mrs Eileen McCarthy, John Mc-Carthy, Pat Murphy, Jerry Sheedy, Noel Curley.

3

The Creamery Manager's Life

The certificate

Isuppose that I was six or seven when I first noticed it - an elaborate coloured Certificate hanging high up on the upstairs landing. It was my father's Creamery Manager's Certificate and now holds a special place in my own home. It was issued in 1925 by the Irish Creamery Managers' Association which eventually 'fell to progress' and became the Dairy Executives' Association.

Prior to the establishment of the Dairy Science Faculty at UCC, those who wanted to manage a creamery were required to carry out an apprenticeship at an operating creamery and then sit an exam set by the Irish Creamery Managers' Association. The certificate, reproduced elsewhere in this book, to my mind was unique for the period, being printed in colour, as well as being distinctive.

There ware eight drawings on the certificate of the main functions of creamery management:

1. The cow herd being milked in the field and the milk being poured into churns on a horse drawn cart;
2. The collection of the milk at the creamery with the farmers' carts awaiting their turn and those finished on their way home;
3. A picture inside the creamery showing the separating of the milk and also the belt drives to the separators and pumps;
4. The churning and other aspects of buttermaking;
5. The mechanical engineering aspects – the source of energy for the operation - the steam boiler and the motive power for driving the main shaft - the steam engine;
6. The scientific issues in testing and quality control laboratory;
7. The marketing and distribution of the manufactured products by road or rail;
8. The offices of financial and commercial functions of the operation.

The certificate was first introduced in 1914 and continued to be awarded until 1932 when the last certificates were issued.

There was a well-structured programme of training in the Albert College Dublin or in Ballyhaise, County Cavan, followed by an apprenticeship at a central creamery followed by a series of exams to be carried out before one could attain this Certificate.

The very unusual and colourful Certificate was issued by the Irish Creamery Managers Association from 1914 until 1932. This is a copy of the Authors' fathers' Certificate.

The programme included instruction in
1. Chemistry and Physics
2. Dairy Farming
3. Dairy Bacteriology
4. Dairy Engineering
5. Creamery Business Methods
6. One year in house training at a central creamery.

My father did his Course in Ballyhaise and his apprenticeship in Garryspillane Co-op in County Limerick, only about two miles from his home. It's strange the way history repeats itself, because about 25 years later, I did my 'practical' training in the same central creamery

One day when I was in Dublin, I called at the office of the Dairy Executives' Association (formerly the Irish Creamery Managers' Association) and asked about the examinations. I was intrigued by the question papers, some of which I have shown in Appendix 2. The original range of subjects and the original course covering three twenty-week modules was first devised by the ICMA.

The UCC course and the UCC Experimental Creamery

The Faculty of Dairy Science was founded at UCC in 1926 and gave its first courses in 1928. The founding academic staff was;

Professor of Dairy Technology, J. Lyons, MSc, ARCScI, NDA, NDD.

Professor of Dairy Chemistry, Dr. G. T. Pyne.

Professor of Dairy Bacteriology, Dr. M. Grimes MSc, PhD.

Professor of Dairy Engineering., F.A. McGrath, B.E.

Professor of Dairy Economics and Accounting, M. Murphy.

Professor of Agriculture, C. Boyle.

The first recipients covered courses from 1925, 1926, 1927, 1928. The 1925 recipients were Aeneas Collins, John T. Donoghue, Joseph Keogh, Denis P. Murphy, Timothy J. Sheehan, Alexander F. E. Stewart and Thomas White.

The courses were run in the new buildings which housed the Experimental Creamery and Institute of Dairy Science, located at University College on Donovan's Road, Cork. The Donovan's Road complex was build at the same time as the beautiful entrance gates and bridge over a channel of the river Lee.

This was the original home of the Faculty of Dairy Science founded in 1924 and started to give the first courses in 1926. The foundation stone was laid on 20th July 1928 and unveiled by William T Cosgrave, then President of the Irish Free State, and Parick Hogan, Minister for Agriculture and Lands.

The first recipient of the BSc (Dairying) UCC, Jeremiah Doherty, with his lecturers and professors, October 30th 1928.

'Institute of Dairy Science, University College Cork. This foundation stone is placed on Friday 20th July 1928 by William T. Cosgrave, LLD., President of the Irish Free State; Patrick Hogan, Minister for Lands and Agriculture; Henry H. Hill B.A., ARIBA, Architect. John Sisk and Son, Construction Company Ltd.

The building was a classical design by Henry H. Hill and was finished in cut limestone. It housed classrooms, laboratories and the unique circular lecture theatre – still in use and of course the University College Experimental Creamery – sadly demolished in 1975. This creamery was a fully functioning commercial creamery but with the secondary function of giving 'hands on' practical experience for the new Creamery Manager's Diploma Course and the Dairy Science Faculty. This was exactly as was recommended by the IAOS committee in 1899 for the training of creamery managers.

During the setting up of the Faculty, there was a face-off as to who would be in control of the creamery – whether the Professor of Agriculture or the Professor of Dairy Technology. In the end the Professor of Dairy Technology won the day and the full title was Professor of Dairy Technology and Director of Creameries. In the 50s the day to day creamery manager was Jack Murphy who also lectured in dairy accounting.

The creamery had some seventy to eighty farmers supplying milk mainly from the farms adjacent to the city. Milk was also delivered from Horgan's cattle exporters holding farms where large numbers of cows were kept while awaiting shipment to overseas 'on the hoof sales'. From 1935, UCC had a branch creamery at Knockraha, near Watergrasshill. This was so that the creamery at UCC could become a central and manufacture dairy products. Knockraha had about 140 suppliers. The UCC creamery also had supply agreements with the following independent auxiliary creameries -

Carragline Co-op Creamery supplied cream - some 20 x15 gallon churns a day. Imokilly Co-op Creamery and its branches at Park, near Youghal, and Ballyrichard, near Midleton. These also supplied cream - about 35 churns containing 23 gallons each, per day.

Ballinhassig Co-op Creamery supplied all cream; about 15 x 23 gallon churns.

Since all the above cream was made into butter, the direct suppliers to the creamery did not have enough milk for the liquid milk trade. This was supplemented by extra milk from the creameries in Terelton, Coachford and Glenville. The milk vendors entered to the right under a beautiful arch to the Experimental Creamery. The milk intake platform for farmers, sadly now gone, was to the right of the arch.

In the mid-50s, the experimental creamery pasteurised milk and sold it to some twenty milk vendors who delivered milk door-to door in the city. They each had their individual milk rounds. The rounds had built up over the years when these milkmen had cows within the city and likely would have paddocks in the city and larger farms outside the suburbs. The milk was delivered loose in churns which had a tap and then a five to eight gallon covered container with a spout. The milkman poured the milk from this container into half-pint, one pint or quart measures and poured it directly into the customer's jug. The delivery was initially by horse drawn milk float and later by van or small truck.

Pasteurisation became common in the 40s before being made compulsory

Suppliers to
Knockraha
branch of UCC
creamery.

The Dairy Science Institute 1930s.

Dairy Science Institute, 1950.

The original Dairy Science building as it is today.

because of the high incidence of Tuberculosis (TB) at the time. This was the standard method for liquid milk up to the entry of bottled milk by Cork Milk Producers (CMP), Ballinahina and Martin Dairies in the early 60s. Some of the vendors at the time were;

Bradley's	O'Leary's	Paddy Kerry	Ron O'Sullivan
Horgan	Buckley	Downeys	Murphys
Long's	Harris	Jack Twomey	Herlihys
Young's	Denis Murphy	Nicky Young	Batt Young
O'Callaghan's.			

Teaching Aspects

In view of its practical teaching and demonstration aspects the experimental creamery had a large variety of equipment. The pasteuriser was an APV plate model with some modifications. The separator was Alfa-Laval – 600 gallons per hour. There was a second separator with a clarifying head for removing sediment and had a mixing head which could be used for standardising to a specific fat percentage.

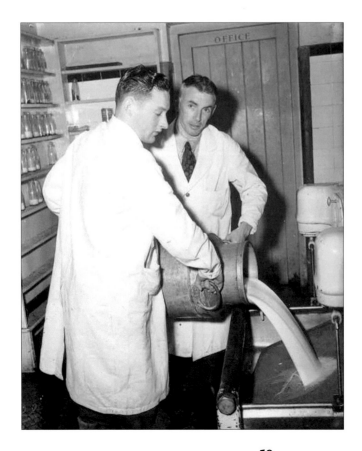

Receiving milk at UCC Experimental Creamery.

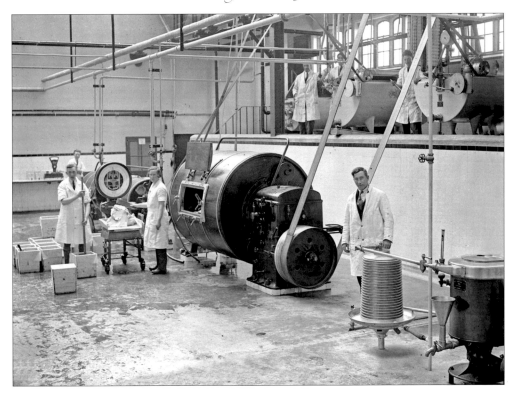

Original buttermaking equipment at University Creamery 1930 (UCC) Buttermaker /buttermaking Instructor, Miss White, is weighing the butter.

Buttermaking

Butter was made on a daily basis and to fully commercial standards under the supervision of Miss White, who hailed from County Westmeath. The butter was packaged in the traditional form of the 1950s – the wooden butterbox. The standard 56lb butterbox was slightly conical and made from white deal wood which was a half-inch thick and nailed using one-inch nails. There were also 28lb boxes which were used for retailing unwrapped butter, commonly sold in the larger grocery shops of the time, including Finlaters in Dublin and Barrys in Cork, who also sold Cheddar cheese off the 56lb or 60lb roll. A small number of 14lb boxes were used for hotels and catering and marked as shown below. Downey's shop in Prince's Street sold butter this way.

One-pound rolls were also packed and wrapped in printed parchment which had the design of the creamery on it. Initially the rolls were made by hand with 'butter pats,' the first semi-automatic with the butter extruded on to a roller table and cut off with wires to form ten or twelve one-pound rolls at a time which were hand wrapped. In a few short years they were fully automatic, the most common being the Benhill. One of the sad losses is that almost all of the hundreds of the unique designs on the 1lb butter wrappers of the 1950s have disappeared.

The UCC Experimental Creamery wrappers were 'University Butter' (a green wrapper up to 1960) and 'Experimental Creamery UCC Butter' (a red wrapper after 1960). No examples of these wrappers are known to have survived. The Registered Number for buttermaking was C.356.

Buttermaking equipment

The cream was cooled using two 400 gallon vats with 'T' stirrer cooled with brine. (calcium chloride and water). The original churns were the traditional timber churns of the time, probably Silkeborg, with a capacity of 35 boxes. These were common in most buttermaking creameries. At that time there were a number of makers including Alborn, Silkeborg, Paasch, Kolding and others, all Danish manufacturers, who were experts in many types of dairy equipment.

These churns were similar in construction to the churn mounted between two supports one of which was the drive unit and gearbox and operating controls. These churns contained internal timber rollers for working the butter, also controlled from the gearbox. These were very efficient and had reached the highest level before the arrival of the 'new shape' churns made in stainless steel. They 'worked' butter without internal rollers. UCC had a Paasch S/S 'cube' churn of 60 box capacity and

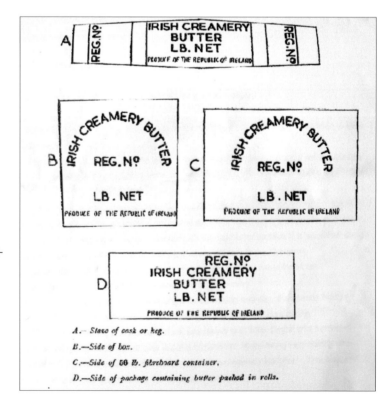

Statutory butter packing marks for butter boxes.

60

Buttermaking in 1950

a Conical (double cone) churn of 25 box capacity made by Kolding.

In 1950, an Alfa-Laval continuous buttermaker was installed for testing. The author can recall from buttermaking, the highlight of the 'practical' was the tea at 'elevenses' with the creamery workers – sweet with plenty of real cream. But no hint of work!!

Cheesemaking

The experimental creamery had a large cheesemaking facility, looked after well by Miss Boyle, from Donegal. Many varieties were made, but the main production was Cheddar (red and white), Gouda, Edam and Caerphilly. In the 1960s, there were two main cheese vats - 3,000 litre vat with overhead carriage, including curd knives and stirrers and also forks for mixing in the salt.

The cheese moulds were telescopic tinned in 28lb, 40lb and 60lb sizes and were pressed in vertical screw presses, later horizontal pneumatic. The cheese was then put into the cheese store to mature. There were two especially designed stores. In the 1950s, there were about 15 persons working in the creamery, in addition to Miss Boyle and Miss White. The creamery was originally powered by a wall shaft with multiple pulleys and belt drives to each separator, pump or churn, driven by a National Oil Engine and later fully electric with individual electric motors on each machine. The shaft was not used in later years, but was not removed until the creamery was demolished in 1975.

I also recall buttermaking in Garryspillane, County Limerickm, and pounding the butter into the 56lb box, having fixed the parchment liners and ensured that they were all overlapped when finished. There was a special roller to finish the top

Original cheese equipment at the University Creamery 1930.

Students cheesemaking in 1950 and Knockraha branch creamery.

butter surface in a 'speckled' design before putting on the top square of parchment which had the Creamery Registration Number, but no name, only 'Irish Creamery Butter' imprinted. This was the same for all creameries and the registration number would have identified the manufacturing creamery. The churn number identified the day and was fully traceable.

One funny incident at UCC was during cheesemaking one day, the cheese being made was Cheddar, which requires a lot of turning of the blocks of curd during 'cheddaring'. The reach was long and the curd block was heavy. 'Miss Boyle' was turning – she reached too far and toppled over into the cheese vat. Recovering very quickly she got out of the vat and, adjusting herself, turned to the creamery workers – 'This blackguarding will have to stop,' and stormed out of the cheese room. (This story was related to me by a person who was present – thanks Noel!)

4
The branch creamery

Mainstay of the co-op movement

Taking the milk to the creamery was a daily event in Irish social history for close on one hundred years. It was an event which was much more than delivering the milk. The creamery was a meeting place, where many important rural activities were initiated and decided on. It was a 'hedge school' where the younger sons of farmers learned more that they did in school but of subjects that would never get on the school curriculum – like buying and selling, bulls and bulling, horses and hunting, fishing and shooting – all the reality of rural life.

At its peak, there were at least 500 branch creameries in Ireland, spread throughout the 26 counties. These branches catered for a rural area, on average three to five miles from the creamery, and each had from about 50 to 350 or more suppliers. Later in the book is a list of the creameries in 1956 and the manages of each, together with other statistical information for that year.

Like any other advance in economic activity, there were the critics. One such critic is described here and taken from *The Irish Co-operative Movement,* by Patrick Bolger.

Knockadea branch creamery.

Opening of new Creamery Castlelyons 1939.
(Irish Examiner)

As in late 1908, Dr John Clancy, Bishop of Elphin, was reported to be reiterating many of the criticisms levelled against the creamery movement from its earliest days:

1. *Children who should be at school were employed to bring milk to the creameries.*
2. *'Morning and evening large numbers assemble in the vicinity of the creameries, and habits of idleness - if not worse vices – are engendered…'*
3. *Public houses near creameries tempted the farmers and frustrated the Church's efforts to promote temperance.*
4. *The art of buttermaking in the home was endangered.*
5. *Families, especially children, were deprived of a proper diet in the interest of 'cupidity of pecuniary profit'.*
6. *There was a danger of spreading germs of contagious diseases through the mixing of milk at the creameries.*
7. *There was no real substitute for whole milk calf-rearing.*
8. *Lack of milk in the home led to inordinate use of tea for domestic purposes – tea without milk and bread without butter: and to the*

introduction of beer and porter for the agricultural labourer in the field….'
9. *The destruction of flourishing local butter markets, followed by the decay of many subsidiary forms of industry... The shipments from our port, the carnage of our quays, the cooperage in a hundred busy workshops.*

The creamery manager was a very important individual in the local community and was held in the same esteem as the parish priest, the doctor or the school teacher.

Going to the creamery was a daily chore for most farmers and was an important part of the day. I can remember my uncle Mick had a special 'creamery pony' and he would get special treatment. The creamery cart was only used for that purpose and there was a special drill in Rahard every morning. Everybody was mustered for milking which entailed getting in the cows – who would be in a nearby field for morning, having the feed and hay in the byres for the cattle, and the churns and strainers were in place. When finished, Auntie Joan would disappear to get the breakfast, the milk cans were readied onto the cart. Then the cart was brought around to collect the previous night's milk in the churns' cool storage. By this time, Uncle Mick would be having his breakfast - bread and butter, boiled eggs, and scalding hot tea with plenty of sugar. When finished, he would hoist himself up on the cart and off to the creamery – the time would be between 7.30 and 7.45am.

One of the last of the warning signs

67

Physical building and Equipment

The creamery was usually a building situated at the edge of a town or village, or often isolated at a crossroads, but always close to a stream or small river. The building stood on its own, as the farmers would enter at one side and moving around the back to exit at the other side for their skim milk. The structure varied from steel frame with metal cladding, to concrete. At the entrance was a wide door with a raised platform outside which would be roughly level with the farmer's cart. Inside this door was a wide area extending 10–15 feet on each side of the door. Directly in front of the door was a large scale which weighed the farmer's milk.

Getting the skim milk in County Kilkenny in 1940.

(G.A. Duncan)

The churns were tipped into a twin tank suspended under the large round dial of the scales. The twin tanks allowed the morning and evening milk to be divided, if required by the manager. These tanks had release valves which allowed the milk to be released once the weight was read and recorded in the platform book and the farmer's passbook. These scales could weigh up to 500 or 1,000lbs of milk at a time in two-pound divisions and were periodically checked and calibrated by the weights and measures sergeant of the Garda Siochana.

Behind the scales there was a big drop in level. The scales emptied into a large divided holding tank corresponding with the divided scales, this tank could hold up to 2,000 gallons of milk (in some of the larger branches). In the early years, milk was all separated as the cream was used to make butter. The skim milk was returned to the farmer for feeding to animals - this practice continued into the mid-50s. If, say, 200lbs (20 gallons) of milk was brought in, then the farmer got back 80% or 160lbs (16 gallons) of skim.

Advertisement from the
'Irish Agricultural and
Creamery Review' for
dial scales 1950s.

Reception scales with
arm scale in pounds.

69

Cromogue creamery branch, county Limerick Branch in 2010.

Drinagh central creamery in 2010.

The lower floor area was where the milk was separated. Depending on the amount of milk the particular branch was handling, there were one or more separators. In addition to the separator there were heaters, coolers, pumps and tanks. These all required either heat or steam, or some form of motive power. In the early days, this came from a vertical hand-fired, coal-fuelled steam boiler which produced steam at about 80 pounds per square inch for the heat, and also motive power through a steam engine – a beautiful smooth engine that moved with a swooch... swooch... and without pollution, but for a hiss of water vapour.

In later years, the steam engines were replaced by a gas oil (diesel) engine (35 horse power National Oil Engine). These were also a very smooth running engine with a four or five foot flywheel like the steam one. The oil engine was much noisier. The big single cylinder going 'putt...putt...putt' – through the silencer over the roof. Starting the steam engine was simple, just opening a valve to let the steam

Steam engine
driving shafting.

into the valve-block. Provided that the boiler pressure was high enough, the engine immediately ran - the oil engine was another story.

One could take a bet the Sunday morning of the big match when everybody was trying to get finished quickly, was the time when the 'bitch' would kick like a spring heifer and decide not to start. Normally to start, a cotton plug was soaked in paraffin oil and lit, then the flame was quenched and the glowing cotton plug was inserted into the cylinder head. The valve lifter was raised and with two persons, the engine driver and the platform man on the handle, the engine was turned faster and faster when with a flick, the engine man would drop the valve lifter and off she went – 'putt... putt... putt'.

However on the 'bitchy' morning after trying this procedure maybe three times and everyone 'gawking' from swinging the handle, the engine man would say 'we'll try the shaggin cartridge'. Tthis was an explosive charge, like a shot gun cartridge

71

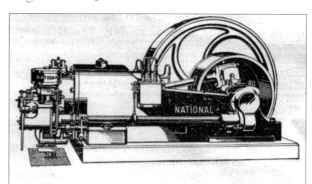

Advertisement in
'Irish Agricultural
and Creamery Re-
view' for National
Oil Engines 1932

Fifty of the leading Creameries in the Free State have installed National Heavy Oil Engines of the type illustrated above. All are unanimous as to the Relia-bility, Economy, Simplicity and Ease of Starting.

without the shot, which was inserted in the cylinder head and was supposed to give the initial power stroke and the high temperature to get the engine going; except they were very temperamental and often did not work. Anyway, many of the early suppliers would well remember being drafted in to swing the handle and complain jokingly that we, the managers and staff, knew 'shagall about engines'. One could count on it that when we were about to give up and call outside help, 'one last shaggin try' worked and off she went!

This engine, whether steam or oil, rotated a long shaft that was mounted high up on the wall of the dairy room, through a series of pulleys. The belt ran through a slot in the wall from the engine room. On this shaft were mounted other pulleys of various diameters so that the various pumps and separators could be run at different speeds. Some of these operated until the 1960s by which time most separators had their own electric motors. The steam boilers were tall vertical types, hand fired by coal and by turf in the war years, which raised many comments - 'Jaes Tom that hoorin' turf from Kerry wouldn't burn in shaggin' hell!'

In later years, these same boilers were successfully converted to oil firing and continued to serve until the branches closed. The last important section of the branch creamery was the skim milk outlet. This was mounted on a raised platform at the opposite side to the milk intake. There was a large funnel about two feet in diameter which hung from a simple spring-dial scales. The height was such that the skim would flow into the churns in the farmer's cart. The funnel was filled by the 'skim man' from the big skim tank near the roof, where the skim was pumped from the separators. The outlet of the funnel had a valve which held in the milk while

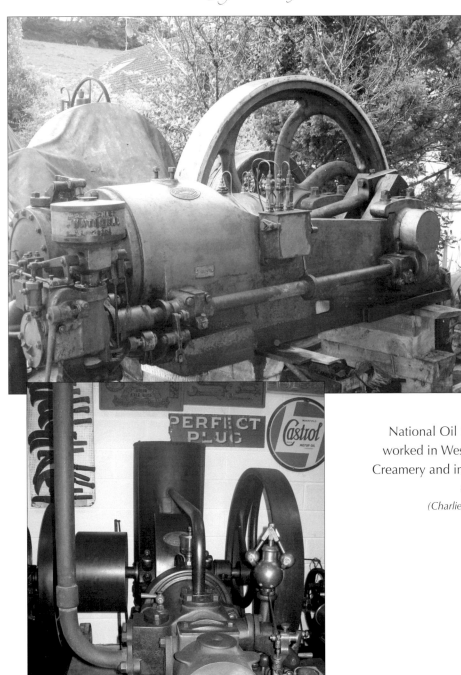

National Oil Engine worked in West Cork Creamery and in many others.
(Charlie Deane)

Hornsby Oil Engine also drove shafting in a creamery *(Charlie Deane)*

Wall shaft on creamery

Early belt driven sep-
arator with open top
feed.

being weighed and could then be released into the churn. This outlet always had a length of cheesecloth or butter muslin around it which was long enough to drop inside the neck of the churn to prevent splashing The skim was weighed out by the 'skim man' who collected the farmer's passbooks from the manager, dispensed the appropriate amount of skim and returned the passbook to the farmer for the following morning.

The main importance of the manager's job was related to the taking in of the milk. This started with the inspection of the milk in the cans or churns. A key person here was the 'platform man' who helped to get the cans onto the platform and remove the lids. A good platform man also had a good 'nose' and could get the 'whiff 'of sour milk the moment the lid came off the can. If he suspected this, he would give the can a flick of his wrist and it would skate across the steel topped floor and stop almost in front of the manager. The politics of this was that the manager would make the final decision. In this way, the platform man could keep his status with the farmers, many of whom were his friends and neighbours.

Having ascertained that the milk was good, the cans were emptied into the scales tank, which could hold up to 1,000lbs in the big size creameries and 500lbs in the smaller branches. It would be very seldom in those years that a farmer's milk would take more than one weighing – over 100 gallons. When all the milk was in the scales, the manager would take the farmers sample bottle from the shelf and put a dipper portion into the bottle, shaking it well to mix it. The milk in the scales was well mixed from the rapid pouring from the cans. This sample would be used to test the milk for fat twice a month.

Having taken the sample, the manager read the milk scales and recorded the weight in the platform book and in the farmer's pass book. In the early days when the supplier took back all the skim milk, this was calculated by the manager and

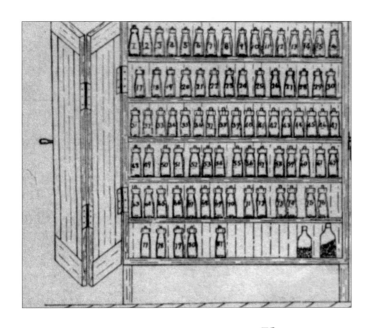

Sketch of milk sample bottle rack.

written into the passbook. If the supplier got butter, this was also recorded in the platform book and in the passbook. In later years the need for ordering A.I. (artificial insemination for cows) was also done at this time.

The amount of skim returned was 80% of the milk received; e.g., if the supplier brought in 240lbs of milk he would get 192lbs of skim back. A few years later in the big cheesemaking co-ops, this return of skim was discontinued and the suppliers were paid some pence more per gallon since the skim contained all of the protein which was the main component of cheese. Initially, the milk was heated to about 30 degrees centigrade (100 farenheit) for the most efficient separation. The skim was pumped to a high level tank above the skim return scales, while the cream was pumped over a cooler and then collected in ten or twenty gallon churns for transport to the buttermaking department in the central creamery.

When the raw milk was collected for cheese, it was cooled and then pumped into the tank on the truck. When full, the driver took it directly to the cheese factory and returned for a second load so that the milk was at its freshest for the cheese.

Social importance of the branch creamery

The creamery system, with its requirement of daily milk deliveries by farmers, created an entirely new social interaction pattern in much of rural Ireland, where it afforded farmers a regular opportunity to come together and discuss current affairs (frequently in public houses located adjacent to the creameries). While much of this consisted of nothing more than gossip and idle chat, these daily meetings also became an important mechanism for the diffusion of information regarding market conditions, prices and technology. The centrality of the local creamery in the social life of dairying regions has been encapsulated in the following passage:

> The creamery is the focal point of a system of intimate and familiar networks of social relationships which have a place of their own in the community and in the everyday lives of many suppliers…In many ways going to the creamery and what it entails takes on a meaning and life of its own, almost independent of the functional purpose it serves.

It is only since the closure of the branch creameries that the importance and influence of this institution has become known and realised. The branch creameries have been part of the rural scene for almost one hundred years. Their loss through closure, often suddenly, has been like a bereavement to many. Creameries were also daily meeting places where the latest news, scandals, dirty jokes, and prices of produce and cattle were obtained. At branch creameries, bargains were won or lost, the 'sure thing' bet on the horses or the dogs was whispered, or the latest 'story' about the 'bastard of a bank manager' was expounded and expanded.

Here too, one heard information on farm sales and debts, new tenants and sad foreclosures. And women! Who was going with who; who was 'shaggin' who; who was a bitch – who was a 'good thing,' who had money, who had feck-all. And drink, the price of the pint, the quality of the pint in various pubs. Poaching – where would you get a salmon or a few pheasants. If you were a greyhound man, where would you get a live rabbit to blood the 'bugger'. If you were a 'horsey man,' who had a good mare; where could you get a good jockey that would 'do what he were told and 'keep his f.....ing mouth shut'! This was also the place for finding out who had a good point-to-point stallion.

The branch creamery was a 'hedge school' for the where the young farming sons learned the ins and outs of rural living outside of their often strict home up bringing. Many arrangements 'to meet 'a suitable young lady' were initiated at the branch.

During election time, whether local for the county council or for the Dáil Éireann (the national parliament), the branch creamery was a favourite meeting and canvassing spot as it ensured a large number of 'possibles' in a single meeting and with much greater certainty. However, many politicians learned to their regret that if they did not have their homework done regarding the farming and agricultural situation, they could sorely suffer from the decision to be there. They dared not arrive in any fancy car, but usually would come with one of the other county council members (in those days you could be in the Dáil and on a county council) from the same party. There would be fierce hand shaking and outlandish promises made. If any of the senior politicians, such as a government minister or the likes, were there there would be the 'minders'. The local Garda would be present in his best uniform with all buttons shining and his boots with 'spit and polish,' by the way directing security and in general making a 'spare prick of him-

Castletownroche Creamery, pictured here, was a typical branch creamery of the 1950s.
(Bill Power Collection)

77

self' - as would be heavily debated on the following morning. It was a great opportunity for the 'heckler' who would do his level best to drive the potential 'politician' into a rage. This was done to the great amusement of the crowd, even those of his own party, but especially with 'independents' who were standing for some obscure purpose or objective.

There was often a county councillor who was also a milk supplier. He would hold his 'clinic' at the branch for a time on most mornings, where he would deal with various requests regarding a variety of requests or queries. How could someone get a medical card, a grant for the new hay barn? Or what was happening with the sheep headage payments, or more recently planning permission for a site, especially if the land was near the coast?

This was the one of the best aspects of the creamery gatherings. The following morning, debates and general slagging following an 'occasion' such as the visit of the Minister; the winning, or losing of a hurling match, or a wedding, or a funeral. In fact, any 'happening' which involved the local rural community was thrashed out. In every creamery branch the local 'wit' could be found. Nobody was safe from this man. He would ridicule anyone in a non-offensive way. Then there was the 'legal brain' who could, would and did debate the finer points of contract law with the best. The 'Doc' was always advising someone how to treat a pain or an ache – whether it was a wife, a cow or a dog. He was often a 'drop out' from medical school because his father had died or because of a financial crises in the family. Bob the Builder (and by that I don't mean the cartoon character) was always solving the building difficulties of some neighbour, whether it was a new barn or an extension to the house or a silage pit. Then, of course, there was the 'healer' who either was a bone setter or a seventh son of a seventh son. The bone man could usually do sprains and joints. Some of the better ones could do 'backs' - this was a favourite with the farming community, since they were always damaging the 'frigging back'. Some of these could fix animals as well as humans, as so often the conversation related to greyhounds and to sport horses.

The Financier was more often the exception; ith a wide knowledge of stocks and shares and very likely a senior co-op committee member, he would be sometimes 'consulted,' rather than asked for advice if some supplier or their relation got a 'windfall' or legacy from a relative in America. No bloody way would they venture near 'them robbers' of shaggin' bank managers (a lesson we would have all done well to heed in recent years, but few of us did). Such was the wide variety of personalities and subjects aired.

The branch creamery was always a favourite spot for the local postman because in those days meeting with the remote farmers at the branch could save him many hours of backbreaking cycling on bad roads and rough 'bohereens'. The postman was also a source of gossip as he often knew the sender of a letter and could tell if it was not only from an official source but nearly who sent it. 'Jaez lads! I'd say Paddy-Joe is after getting the grant for his silage pit,' or 'Young Carthy is going to court next month for batin' the shite out of the Poacher Murphy's young fella last March. That Murphy shagger is fierce dangerous, he'd sue his mother'. 'There's three American letters today, an' that I'd say is lumps of dollars for the Christmas'.

Then there were the practical jokers- some with really nasty ideas. Mickey Joe was a martyr for the drink. Every morning following taking his few gallons of milk to the central branch he would drive the donkey and cart up the street and tie the reins to the ESB pole outside Walsh's pub. He would then disappear behind pint after pint until the barman threw him out. Meanwhile, our jokers, having given him time to get 'nicely,' would untackle the donkey from the cart, then pull the cart so that the pole was between the shafts. They would retackle the donkey, now fixed immoveably, with the pole behind the donkey's arse. Later in the day when Mickey Joe came out to go home, he was so 'flutered' with porter that after trying a few times to move, just lay back and fell into a drunken sleep. He would finally wake some time in the late night hours. Now fully sober, he would curse the jokers to high heaven, and release the cart from the pole and the donkey would take him home.

My Dad, Patrick Quish, was a branch creamery manager for close on fifty years. He remembered well cycling around the countryside near Mitchelstown canvassing the farmers with the general manager, Eamon Roche (better known locally as 'The Boss Roche'), to form new branches in competition with the then English-owned Newmarket Dairy Company. He later had a Douglas motorcycle that had a twin cylinder horizontally opposed engine. It was a sophiscated machine in those days which I'm sure he did not appreciate as he was not technically orientated.

There was tough competition in the initial stages when the co-op actually built

Most common transport in branch creameries in the 1940s and 50s.

Douglas
motorcycle 1927

new branches within 100 yards of the competition. But the English companies recognized that a new era had arrived and their day was over. They finally sold the remaining branches to the new co-op. There were ten branches within about a ten mile radius of the central in Mitchelstown, with suppliers ranging from two or five gallons a day to those with more than one hundred gallons and with numbers of suppliers in the branches from 30 to more than 300. This same pattern was repeated around the country.

Other branch services

These branches initially operated as milk collecting centres and then started to separate the milk, returning the skim milk to the farmer and sending the cream to

Ballyclough branch near Mallow.
(Bill Power Collection)

80

Derelict branch creamery at Corroghgurm, near Mitchelstown.
(Bill Power Collection)

the central to be made into butter. The branch also developed a local store which supplied feed for pigs, concentrates for cows and other farm supplies which were used on a daily basis. Fertiliser and other supplies, such as timber and cement for building, could also be ordered in the store. Once a week, the branch bought eggs from the farmers' wives. These were checked for breakage, counted and packed into the special egg boxes which were marked with the supplier's number. When they got to the central egg store, they were light checked for good/bad and then graded for size. The grading machine was a sophisticated piece of equipment which had a large circular table divided into five sections – pullets, small, medium, large and extra large. The eggs were first checked with a light box which showed if an egg was bad (known as a 'glugger'). The passed eggs were then placed in a sloping tray which fed the eggs past a series of 'gates' of different sizes and were then collected in the appropriate grade section. All the surfaces of the machine were covered with green baize to protect the delicate eggs which were then packed in grades boxes of twelve dozen for the markets. Payment was made directly to the wives by the creamery manager, which was a great incentive to produce eggs. This was a profitable operation for the co-op because in those days there were no specialist egg producers and the farms were the main source of eggs for the city markets and trade in Dublin and Cork. The eggs were shipped to these markets by train from the local station. In later years, when the railways closed, they were shipped by truck.

Ballinamona creamery on the Mitchelstown to Mallow road.
(Bill Power Collection)

The salmon poachers

One spring morning in the central branch, there was a real 'buzz' that went all the way from the last supplier right up to the creamery platform. 'Who has it this time,' says Jim to Ned O'Keeffe in the next cart back. 'Who has what?' says Ned, pulling on his pipe and reluctantly lifting his head from the racing page of the *Cork Examiner*. 'Christ! But you're a cool wan,' Jim answers, 'the frigging water bailiff is after passing down Toarpy's corner and heading down here, somewan must have shaggin fish!' Ned moved; the glasses were removed, the paper folded and put under the folded bag he used as a seat on the horse and cart. Slowly removing his pipe, he points the stem towards Jim and slowly an calmly says 'there's two eight pounders in the 10 gallon can. Now say nuttin' and don't get excited. One is for the Boss's wife and she's taking the other for the golf club open day on Sunday. All we have to do is get them to John in the butter office.

Jim looked at Ned, realisation dawning. 'Jasus you're some feckin' chancer! Now don't walk me into the shite'. 'No fear of that. Tom is due out from the cheese factory any minute. Where's that bollix of a bailiff now?' asks Ned. 'He's not into the yard yet,' says Jim, 'and here's Casey with the trolley. Casey struggled across the wide yard with a flat bed trolley on which were two ten gallon cans. Showing the intention of crossing the yard, he has to pass through the line of waiting farmers. He veered slightly so as to pass between Jim and Ned. With a quick look around, Ned whips the churn with the salmon from the cart onto the trolley and with a deft follow through, lobbed one of Casey's cans onto the cart. Casey pushed the trolley through the gap between Jim and Ned and continued across to the egg store behind

Early Ballyclough headed paper logo.

the butter store. Here the salmon were removed from the milk, rinsed and put safely away for the Boss's wife.

Outside, Ned smiled at Jim. 'Now what did I tell ye, not a bit of bodder, but these shaggers are too smart - they must be getting the tip-off'. Suddenly there was commotion. Just inside the yard gate a young farmer's son, of about 16 years of age, was seen racing across the yard and in the back door of the cheese factory, with the fat dumpy bailiff puffing after him shouting, 'come back here you little hoor! I know you have a fish,' as he disappeared into the factory. No sooner had the bailiff gone out of sight than the runner's father slipped quickly into the kitchen of the factory canteen with a newspaper wrapped bundle. He was out in an instant and was lighting up his pipe beside his cart when the bailiff reappeared and walked over to this man, Gerry. Now out of breath, the bailiff asked 'was that your young fella that ran'. Struggling for breath after the exertion, Gerry replied 'that's right. 'I sent him into Mary to book a can of whey for the pigs. Anything wrong'? Gerry continued, 'You know effing well that someone has salmon here and I'm going to sort them out,' the bailiff retorted sourly. 'Well,' says Gerry, 'I've none. Anyhow they're too much like trouble'. He moved the cart forward a few steps nearer the intake platform and lit up his pipe.

This is the actual branch in the 'The Salmon Poachers'.
(Bill Power Collection)

Ned, his pipe in full steam took out his *Cork Examiner*, studied the racing page for a moment and turning to Jim said 'I feel lucky to day. There's a horse going in Navan today called "Bailiffs Folly". He's 20/1. He could win you know'. He winked at Jim and, of course, he did win.

Testing day at the branch

All suppliers' milk was tested twice a month for butterfat percentage. This was the basis of payment for milk delivered during that particular month. The timing was not fixed but was usually about mid-month and a few days before the month's end. Since the creamery purchased milk for the purpose of making butter only, it was not interested in the skim milk which was returned to the farmer and which was used to feed calves, pigs and other farm livestock. So payment was made to the farmer for the weight of butterfat purchased and which was established by testing the milk for butterfat content.

This test was very important to both the farmer and also to the creamery, since one could be underpaid and the other could pay too much. Throughout the years since butter was first made on a commercial scale there have been many tests for butterfat. The tests on milk which were directly related to the payment were always a source of argument and debate in farming circles – and indeed still are to this day.

The testing accuracy was checked by the Department of Agriculture's Dairy Produce Inspector who, on a periodic basis, check tested a number of samples already done by the creamery manager. Because the test was directly related to the payment it needed to be accurate, easy to carry out and capable of being carried out quickly – even the largest branch being done in one day.

In 1850, the first cheese factories were opened in Ireland. These of course bought milk at an agreed price per gallon since they required all of the milk and not just the cream. Similarly, this procedure also applied to the condensed milk factories, which first appeared in the 1870s. Both the cheese factories and condensed milk factories were not large or numerous, and there was not much difficulty then with butterfat. In 1870, the cream collecting creameries started and these grew very quickly. Because they had a large number of suppliers with different fat contents, it was important to have an agreed method of fat determination.

The earliest method of determining the butter content of the cream received at a cream collecting creamery was to churn separately in a small tin can (about a pint) of each supplier's milk and to weigh the butter obtained. The butter content of all the milk/cream delivered by each supplier was then calculated on the basis of the butter yield of the sample churned.

While this method of getting the butter content of suppliers' milk/ cream by churning small samples was not a very accurate one, it nonetheless provided a more

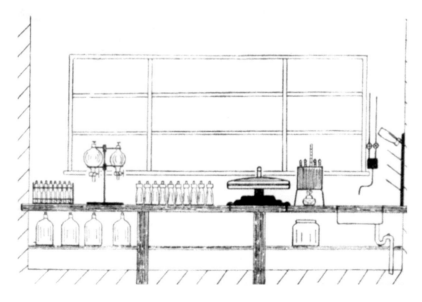

Sketch of typical testing bench in branch creamery

equitable basis for assessing the value of cream than that of measure only.

The Gerber Fat Test was invented in 1892 and athough it used two chemical re-agents it has proved to be easily taught to relatively non-scientific workers. It became the most common fat test in Europe and indeed, in all of Russia, as I discovered in later years during my travels in that part of the world. It is still used in many developing countries.

The organisation of the testing was the key to doing all the tests in one day, starting when the milk intake was finished. The samples were taken daily on a composite basis and placed in the sample bottle. This bottle had a milk preservative tablet in it and a few ounces of lead shot which helped to mix the contents when shaken. Testing day saw the sample bottles laid out in batches of 36 (two rows of 18) on the testing bench. In most branch creameries, the Gerber Centrifuge would take 36 test tubes at a time and these were standing in a rack in front of the sample bottles.

Using an automatic glass measuring flask, the sulphuric acid was added to each test tube, then the milk was added to each from the appropriate sample. This addition was required to be carried out by the manager. This was then followed by addition of amyl alcohol. Then the test tubes were corked and, using a special cover, all 36 tubes were shaken together. While still very hot due to the chemical reaction, they are placed in the centrifuge and spun at 1,100 rounds per minute for five minutes.

When I started, many smaller branches had hand operated centrifuges but later

Photo of milk testing tubes and associated items.

all were electric with heaters and timers. (An example of the hand centrifuge can be seen in the Cork Butter Museum). The tubes are then placed in a hot water bath at 150°F (65.55 degrees centigrade) and read off on the scale of the test tube one by one when the test result in written into a special test record book. Any test suspected of being incorrect or abnormal would be repeated.

Testing day was a busy one and good organisation was always a key to a smooth operation. Then of course there were the stories and the smart 'boyos' who tried to manipulate the result in order to get a higher monthly average test and therefore more money for their milk. The same old tricks came up time after time sometimes with variations but they were inevitability found out. Some of the means were like this; adding cream to the milk – could be expensive and loose more the gained; adding goats' milk to the milk – which could be as high as seven or eight per case;

Electric Gerber Centrifuge.

tampering with the samples – even though the sample cupboard was always locked when all the milk was in one could never be sure but that some hoor found a way

Whatever the means it was very difficult to beat the system since one look at the historic range for that supplier would reveal that all was not normal. The standard of testing of managers was periodically checked by the Dairy Produce Inspector, who worked for the Department of Agriculture. He would take five random samples and test them the results should be within 0.10 of what the manager got. I'm not sure what the penalty for bad testing was but it was more hurt pride to have it right.

And then there was the other side of the coin – the twisted manager to drunk to test and who pours all the sample bottles into a bucket or two and then does two or three tests and distributes them to the suppliers. More often he would just pour the samples down the drain and make up the tests especially if he was late going to the Limerick Junction races.

There was sometimes complaints from suppliers about the test they got and it would be normal for the manager to re-do a test with the supplier present to restore confidence of course there were some 'pigs' of managers and who would feel that their superior knowledge and skill was being questioned. Equally so there were some crazy arrogant farmers who would not believe the re test, in this case the complaint was referred to the central laboratory which would probably satisfy the irate supplier.

One of the chemicals used in milk testing is amyl alcohol which had a magnetic attraction for certain individuals. These could be from a variety of persons with knowledge of the process and with little care as to the source or purity of the liquid as long as it contained alcohol.

Unfortunately some did not know the dangers or in some cases chose to ignore them, amyl alcohol is a dangerous poison; it will kill and has killed. I can recall at least five who died from drinking the chemical - three were workers in a branch, two were found dead in a corner of the boiler room and the third beside the half empty bottle in the testing room. One middle-aged branch manager was found dead in his car with half a naggin bottle of the stuff on the front seat. The day after a break-in at a West Limerick branch, a local farmer, well known for his drink problem, was found dead in the corner of his hay barn.

While this was the extreme side of the dangers, there were a few other nasty accidents and at least one criminal act involving the use of milk testing materials. I recall a potentially serious accident in which I was personally involved. We were testing in the central branch and utilising the cheese factory laboratory. We had placed 36 tubes in the electric centrifuge. A lab assistant was washing glassware at a sink beside the centrifuge. The centrifuge speeded up and was at full speed for about two minutes out of five when (as we discovered later) the spindle sheared and the spinning tray and cover with 36 hot test tubes pushed through the top cover and spraying hot sulphuric acid all around the walls. Broken test tubes flew and one caught Mary, the lab assistant, on the arm and lacerated it with a nasty cut. My lab coat was sprayed with hot acid.

Luckily, Jimmy Norris was hosing the floor outside the laboratory door and quick as a flash he had raised the hose and drenched Mary and myself with cold water from top to bottom – thus saving us from acid burns. The lab was a mess. The tests had to be redone, Mary's arm needed four stitches but, apart from my lab coat, I was not affected by the acid – all thanks to the quick thinking of Jimmy Norris.

A criminal case - or was it – occurred in the late 1960s. The accepted likely occurrence of events is that a gang – criminal or possibly para-military, raided a northern bank premises by breaking in through the roof one summer weekend. Knowing that the manager and his family were away (they lived on the premises),

BALLYCLOUGH
CO-OPERATIVE CREAMERY LIMITED

MILK ACCOUNT

M _____ No. _____

Month Ending _____ 19 _____

Please return at once if found incorrect

Date	New Milk	Butter Lbs.	
1			
2			
3			
4			
5			
6			
7			
8			
9			
10			
11			
12			
13			
14			
15			
16			
17			
18			
19			
20			
21			
22			
23			
24			
25			
26			
27			
28			
29			
30			
31			
TOTAL			

Milk will be paid for strictly according to quality as ascertained at the Creamery, and anyone found sending adulterated milk will forfeit all money due.

General Average Test _____ % General Average Price _____ p per gallon

Any errors or irregularities to be reported within 2 days to Manager.

Farmer's Platform milk record card.

Platform book.

No.	Lbs. or Galls.	Lbs. Butter	No.	Lbs. or Galls.	Lbs. Butter	No.	Lbs. or Galls.	Lbs. Butter	No.	Lbs. or Galls.	Lbs. Butter
1			51		6	101	1446	9	151		
2			52			102			152		22
3	364	1	53	130	1	103			153	192	
4	74		54	1272		104	750		154	792	5
5	300		55	346		105	612	1	155	852	
6			56	670		106	726	1	156		
7			57			107			157		
8	630		58	1076	1	108			158		
9			59			109			159		
10			60			110			160	674	
11			61	1342		111			161		
12			62			112			162		
13			63	1286		113	924		163	132	
14			64			114			164		
15			65			115			165		
16	60		66			116	186	1	166	94	
17			67	5102		117	162		167		
18			68			118			168	1226	1
19			69			119			169		
20			70			120			170	520	1
21	1400	2	71	20		121	492		171	114	
22			72	190		122	1998	2	172		
23			73			123	838		173	5	
24			74			124			174		
25			75	1620		125	446	1	175	38	
26			76			126			176		
27	742	2	77	304		127	446		177	44	
28	308		78			128			178	38	
29			79			129			179	1234	
30	958		80	48		130	272	2	180		
31	1804		81			131	1744		181	80	

CREAMERY Date 28 - ? - 19 ?

a large safe was hoisted out and taken to a disused barn where it was worked on using various implements and tools to try to open it. Among the items found afterwards was a Winchester quart bottle of sulphuric acid, later traced to a local branch creamery, with which they tried to burn the lock mechanism. In frustration, they finally dumped the safe in a local pond where it was found weeks later. When finally opened by an expert, all the cash totalling £45,000, was found very wet but none the worse for wear.

Doing the end of month branch accounts

Doing the accounts was the culmination of each month and a busy two weeks for the branch creamery manager. The last day of the month meant the completion of the second round of fat tests and the removal of all the milk samples from the sample rack and getting the clean sample bottles ready for the new month. This entailed putting a preservative tablet into each bottle and also about two or three ounces of lead-shot, and then finally ensuring that the farmer's number was legible. It was usual to do the testing on the last day of the month unless it fell on a Sunday, when the test would then be done on the Monday. The results were written into the milk tests journal beside the mid-month test and the average worked out and recorded.

With the testing completed, the next task was totting all the farmers' platform cards, which was the definitive record of the milk supplied by each farmer during the said month. In those days there were no computers, so accurately totting each farmer's milk was a required skill. It was a log tot with 30 or 31 lines of mainly three figures. When we were studying in UCC, Professor Mick Murphy had a weekly totting test and one was required to get one hundred per cent accuracy. Those of us who found it difficult - like myself - dreaded these tests but we later thanked him. I had one other problem. If I was at home when my Dad was doing the accounts, he would toss me five or six platform cards and say 'do those and I'll check if you are getting any better' – I hated that. He could tot a platform card in thirty seconds!

So with all the platform cards totalled, the milk totals were written into the branch accounts book, called a Summary Book, and the definitive Branch Accounts Record. Each farmer had a line which was identified by his supply number. So we have total milk supplied followed by the average butter fat test, next is total pounds of butter fat supplied, which when multiplied by the price per pound of butterfat (which varied on a monthly basis) gave the total value of the milk supplied that month. An example may help. Total milk supplied 6,600lbs x 3.4% fat = 224.4lbs of butterfat x 52.3 pence/lb = £48-18-0.

This for about twenty gallons per day from some five or six cows, which was a good income in the 50s. The butterfat calculations were speeded up through the use of a special ready reckoner developed for a variety of prices of butterfat per pound. At about this time, there was a new electronic calculator in the branch manager's office - just one between ten managers. The competition to get use of it was fierce.

No.	NAME	Dr. Balance Brought forward £ s. d.	Advances Amount £ s. d	Date	Interest and Notes £ s. d.	Butter £ s. d.	Mill Stuffs and Grinding £ s. d.	Sundry Sales A s. £ s. d.	Skim M Gals.	Price
1	Dl Aherne		2 - -	9c6/25		2 7 3				
2	Sean Barrol					2 7 3				
3	Reps Mrs J. Cotter	78 4 2								
4	Jerh Mc Sweeney	44 17 10				5 3 -				
5	Wll Buckley	36 5 6				2 15 10		1 10 -		
6	Reps Wll Bradley					2 15 10		15 -		
7	Jas. Galalane					5 7 4		15 -		
8	George Plunkett	52 11 3				3 8 8		15 -		
9	Thos Kelleher	48 6 1								
10	Wll Brown					2 11 6		15 -		
11	Dr Murphy	44 1 9			2 7	1 1 6				
12	Bos Lucey					3 8 8		15 -		
13	John D Barrol					1 5 9				
14	Wll C. Hallahan					4 14 5				
15	John Forde	56 12 -			2 3					
16	Reps John Twomey					4 4		1 5 -		
17	Jas. Droney									
18	Jerome Fitzgerald					1 14 4				
19	Tim O Leary					4 4		15 -		
20						4 4				

Pages from Branch Summary Book.

I can recall it was a FACIT.

So with the total milk value computed, we go to the debit side of the Summary Book which had a series of columns to enter the supplier's purchases for the month. These would be pounds of butter taken (the author can recall when the average butter consumption per capita in Ireland was 27lbs per head per year, which I think was the highest in the world at that time). Items purchased from the store could include feed for cattle, pig ration, poultry, hardware items such as binder twine, rope, wire timber etc; then there were other services such as A.I., ploughing seed and seed dressing and so on. The list was wide and depended on the farmer and his operation. The amount to be paid by the farmer would be decided by the manager who was very familiar with the circumstances of each farmer and made a judgement based on this knowledge. So the debits were totalled and when calculated the amount of the monthly cheque was determined.

When the Summary Book was squared, the preparation of the final documents would be done, the main item being a statement of account based on the entries in the Summary Book. we itemised everything and when this was complete the individual cheques were written. These were required to be completed by a specific date, since they had to be signed by two committee members from the branch, as

SUMMARY OF SUPPLIER'S ACCOUNTS AND PAYMENTS

ER'S NAMES	Galls. Whole Milk Supplied	Av. Test	Lbs. B. Fat Therein	Price per lb.	Value of Milk Supplied	Balance forward due to Supplier	CREDITS Skim	Cash	Refund (Wilewar)		Total Credits	Tota
					5804 6 5						5957 24 153	
mount forward	66323				5804 6 5	1 5 7.	148 17 10	20 0 0	7 12 6		41 6 11	
	479	3·75	20·72		41 6 11						10 0	
						10 0		·			13 5 3	
	139	3·90	21·55		12 9 7.		15 8				12 10 3	
	151	3·60	19·89.		12 10 3						37 12 1	
	359	4·55	25·14		37 12 1						24 9 0	
	244	4·25	23·45		23 17 6		11 6				102 6 7	
	1125	3·95	21·83		102 6 7.						41 0 6	
	495	3·60	19·89		41 0 6						4 5 10	
	46	4·05	22·38		4 5 10						67 7 3	
	739	3·75	20·72		63 15 11		3 11 4				8 8 0	
	96	3·80	21·00		8 8 0						14 15 10	
	163	3·40	21·55		14 12 8		3 2				9 10	
						9 10					11 7	
						11 7					6 22	
	77	3·45	19·06		6 22						150 910	
	1660	3·80	21·00		145 5 0		5 4 10					

Monthly accounts.

well as the general manager. In Mitchelstown, this was usually done in the head office at King Square, which we knew as 'Kingstons'. The two committee men designated to sign were always delighted as they got £10 each for petrol and their lunch paid for at the local hotel; so there was no shortage of volunteers for the job. The only rule was that a committee member could not sign the cheques from his own branch.

With all the paperwork complete, all that remained was collating the items and putting them into envelopes for distribution. I well remember my Dad bringing home the documents and spreading the various bundles in the big sitting room table. He would collect one item from each bundle and when collected would fold them inside the month's passbook. He would then hand it to me to insert into the envelope. When some twenty were finished, the table was full so he would damp the glue on the envelope with warm water and stick it closed and then place the first twenty in a box with the supplier's number on top. We would then start the next twenty until they were all finished.

There was great excitement at the Creamery on the 'cheque day'. Suppliers hunched in groups comparing 'fat tests' and other issues like 'how much was deducted for the store'. 'I expected a higher test this month'. A few of the 'usuals' retired to the local bar for a few 'scoops'. The monthly cheque was the only constant income to most farms who didn't have EU or Government subsidies to depend on. No matter how small, the creamery cheque made a big contribution to the living standards of the rural families, and changed country living forever.

Store goods receipt, 1959.

The alcohol gun

This was started by the new cheese expert, John McCarthy, and was aimed at improving the quality of milk for cheesemaking. I well remember one of the first days of the 'clean up'. I was at this time working in the cheese factory laboratory and was drafted in by John to help. We arrived at Ballindangan branch unannounced at about 8.00am, and wearing our official white coats climbed onto the next farmer's cart. 'Mac' whipped off the lid of the churns and sticking his head down near the open can had a good smell - it passed. Then on to the next and the next, until he turned to me and asked me to smell also. It is very sour, so Mac turned to the farmer and declared 'this is sour. You'll have to take it home. Its no good to the creamery'.

The farmer complained to the branch manager, Jackie Rea, who in his inimitable cool drawl replied 'well if Mr McCarthy says he doesn't want your milk there's nothing for it but take it home and feed it to the calves – and don't have it sour again, 'cos from today it's a different game'. There was some silent cursing and swearing but the milk went home and a lesson was learned. The testing continued and five other farmers got their 'take it home' orders that day, one bring so angry that he threw the churn off the cart, spilling it, with such venom that he frightened the horse who took off up the road. At the narrow bend, the horse went straight through the hedge ending upside-down with the poor horse shaking with fright and the other two churns spilled into the dyke. The comments back at the creamery

Above - A creamery cheque.

Below: Wage rates, 1948.

Joint Labour Committee Order
CREAMERY WORKERS' WAGE INCREASE

The Labour Court's Creameries Joint Labour Committee has made an order fixing new minimum wage rates for employees affected by the Committee. The new weekly rates are set out below vis-a-vis the rates fixed by order of the Committee since 1948.

Creameries:	13.8.'48	4.11.'49	24.8.'51	26.9.'52	2.10.'54	13.10.'56	15.2.'58	6.2.'60
	s. d.	s. d.	s. d.	s. d.	s. d.	s. d.	s. d.	s. d.
Maintenance Mechanic, Fitter	100/-	105/-	111/-	123/6	128/6	137/-	147/-	157/-
Buttermaker, Cheesemaker	80/-	85/-	91/- M.	103/6 M.	108/6 M.	117/- M.	127/- M.	137/- M.
			89/- F.	101/6 F.	106/6 F.	115/- F.	125/- F.	135/- F.
Assistants do.	75/-	80/-	86/- M.	98/6 M.	103/6 M.	112/- M.	122/- M.	132/- M.
			84/- F.	96/6 F.	101/6 F.	110/- F.	120/- F.	130/- F.
Enginemen, Firemen, etc.	72/6	77/6	83/6	96/-	101/-	109/6	119/6	129/6
Lorry Driver	72/6	77/6	83/6	96/-	101/-	109/6	119/6	129/6
All other Females:								
1st Year	30/-	32/-	34/-	38/-	41/-	46/-	51/-	56/-
2nd Year	37/6	40/6	42/6	46/6	49/6	54/6	59/6	65/6
3rd Year	45/-	49/-	53/-	61/6	64/6	69/6	74/6	81/6
4th Year	55/-	60/-	64/-	72/6	77/6	82/6	87/6	95/6
All other Males:								
18-19 years	50/-	52/6	56/6	65/-	70/-	78/6	83/6	90/6
19-20 years	60/-	63/6	67/6	76/-	81/-	89/6	94/6	102/6
20 years and over	65/-	70/-	76/-	88/6	93/6	102/-	112/-	122/-
Cream-Separating Stations:								
All Workers								
18-19 years	50/-	52/6	56/6	65/-	70/-	78/6	83/6	90/6
19-20 years	55/-	58/6	62/6	71/-	76/-	84/6	89/6	97/6
20 years and over	60/-	65/-	71/-	83/6	88/6	97/-	107/-	117/-

were such: 'Jas! when Biddy sees the cart and hears about the spilt milk she'll have his guts for garters. That wan has a fierce temper'. And so the cleanup went to another branch. The following day in Ballyhooly, Mac adopted a different approach and produced a shiny kettle like object from the car. It had a long spout with a slot in it and a small glass container at the other end. With the lid off the churn he pushed the long spout into the milk. He then lifted it out ande turned the spout up in the air. The milk flowed into the glass container mixing with a clear liquid and stayed ok. 'This is fine,' said Mac, taking off the glass container and spilling out the milk mixture. He rinsed it in a bucket of water and replaced it on the implement.

Being intrigued I asked Mac what it was. 'It's an alcohol gun,' he replied, with one of his rare grins. 'Here's how it works. We have absolute alcohol on the container. The spout picks up a measure of milk and is deposited in the glass container with an equal measure of alcohol. If the milk is over 0.2% lactic acid, the milk will curdle and we send it back. We will use this from now on to check every branch on a monthly basis'.

This proved to be a breakthrough in forcing an improvement in milk quality. The farmers realised very quickly that cooling the milk ensured that it did not fail the alcohol gun. From this time on, an extra payment was made for not returning the skim milk as the full cream milk was increasingly used to make high quality cheese in some nine varieties of natural cheese and an increasing range of processed cheeses. This all came about through the technical expertise of John McCarthy, and the efforts on the cheese floor of the head cheesemaker, Mollie Gallagher., a native of Donegal These innovations in starter technology and in cheese production were world firsts and must be acknowledged as such. In later years, John McCarthy was associated with TMS, an International consulting group, which helped many developing countries, mostly in Africa, in their development of dairy processing and the progression of their food security programs. I was privileged to be involved in this work in recent years, my first introduction being obtained through John McCarthy to Zambia in Africa in 1990, where I was involved in making Cheddar and Edam cheese in Mazabuka.

And so the year of the Alcohol Gun began with myself, then training in two new young dairy scientists to continue the improvement of milk quality in the remaining eight branches and also in some outside creameries which supplied milk for cheesemaking. Anyway the 'daring duo' with the Alcohol Gun ventured out with the full authority of Mitchelstown Creameries' cheese department to reject milk if it failed the alcohol test. The results were very good but not without some grief to our heroes. We were never told it directly, but there were many stories in the pubs about the 'little hoors with their fucking alcohol gun' and 'getting it shoved where the monkey stuck the nut'. Apparently, one of the other lads with the Alcohol Gun was thrown into the milk tank. Another got a flake of a hurley, while both were also offered farmer's daughters in marriage.

Dromcollogher Co-operative Creamery Museum

It is essential that this special place is protected from deterioration and promoted as an educational and social exhibit of our rural heritage on the international tourist trail.

The museum was opened on 6 June 1889 and is a testimony to the major contribution that co-ops have made to the social, cultural and economic fabric of rural Ireland over the past one hundred years.

This is a unique exhibition based on the original Dromcollogher Co-op Dairy Factory Society Ltd.

ICOS

The ICOS was founded in 1894 as the IAOS (Irish Agricultural Organisation Society) by Sir Horace Plunkett. Its formation was a turning point in the development of Agriculture in Ireland and in particular the development of the Dairy Industry which was at a serious crossroads with increased competition in the quality Buttermarkets and the invention of the Mechanical Separator and Butterchurns and their use by the proprietary creameries.

Horace Plunkett saw the need to keep ownership of creameries on farmers control and to reduce the power of the proprietary creameries with the eventual objective of ridding them from the Industry altogether.

In the early days of the IAOS there were a small number of very powerful intellects including Horace Plunkett, Robert Anderson, AE(George Russell), Balfour and of course Fr Finlay.

There was no Department of Agriculture in these early days and no national policies on Agricultural or Dairy Industry development and no control. The Butter Markets around the country were flourishing but apart from the still highly successful Cork Butter Exchange the quality aspects were not really good and the IAOS saw the need for more regulation, not only in Quality but in manufacturing methods and in quality milk production and in increasing yields of milk and in Qualified Personnel.

This gap was taken up by the IAOS who had a technical section that in its early days had no competition. It was the IAOS which provided the working Model Dairy for the 1903 Cork Exhibition called the Daffodil Dairy. Many trials were carried out by individual Co-ops to promote silage making, improvement of yield etc. This technical section was headed up by Thomas Fant Chief Engineer of the Society, W.J. Ebrill BE was appointed in 1932 as Adviser on creamery Plants.

Following meetings of Plunkett's famous Recess Committee the Department of Agriculture and Technical Instruction was set up in 1899 with Plunkett as Vice-President. Without the ICOS/IAOS the Co-op Movement in Ireland would probably never have happened. To day it is the Umbrella Organisation for all types of Co-operatives and down through its more than 115 years has been blessed with some of the best Organisers and Executives in the Country, CEOs were R.A. Anderson, Dr. Henry Kennedy, Paddy Kelly, John McCarrick, Jim Moloney and John Tyrrell The Presidents of the ICOS all came from Co-op Agricultural Societies.

For more detail on the ICOS readers are referred to; 'The Irish Co-operative Movement,' Pat Bolger IPA, 1977. 'Fruits of a Century,' 100 Years history, ICOS, 1994.

Farmers support organisations and the media

As the creameries developed, it became clear that even though they were co-ops under farmers control, they could still control milk prices and likewise the Department of Agriculture controlled other aspects of farming activity. These actions pointed to the need for farmers organisations, to speak for the farmers at co-op and at Government level.

The first of these voluntary organisations was **Muintir na Tire**, founded by Canon John Hayes in 1937. Muintir was concerned with rural and community development and since then it has been the harbinger of numerous initiatives. In the years up to 1960, it promoted community halls, and centres, developed turf cutting schemes during the Second World War, encouraged the acceptance of Rural electrification, involved in the Limerick Rural Survey and also the beginning of Group Water Schemes in Rural areas. It piloted Community information Centres and local Credit unions – really amazing achievements.

In 1944, **Macra na Feirme** was founded by Stephen Cullinan (a rural science teacher) as a organization for young people between 17 and 35 years of age. The organisation's original purpose was to provide young farmers with adequate training to ensure their livelihood and to provide an outlet for socialising in rural areas. Macra na Feirme was adopted as the official title of the organisation in December 1946. 'Macra' means 'stalwarts' or 'the elite,' and 'na feirme' means 'of the land'. The organisation has a nation-wide network of clubs with six key areas of activity: agriculture, sports, travel, public speaking, community involvement and performing arts. Macra na Feirme established
* The *Irish Farmers Journal*
* Irish Creamery Milk Suppliers Association
* Macra na Tuaithe (now Foroige)
* National Farmers' Association (now IFA)
* Farm Apprenticeship Scheme
* Irish Farm Accounts Co-op (IFAC)
* National Co-operative Farm Relief services Ltd.

Among its National Presidents are all the giants of Irish Agriculture over the years.

The **Irish Creamery Milk Suppliers' Association** is the oldest of the farming organisation's, being formed in 1950. It is particularly strong in ensuring fair milk prices from co-ops and has continued to develop its range of committees and activities and is a strong political lobbyist.

The **Irish Farmers' Association** is one of the most powerful lobby groups in Irish politics and started as the National Farmers Association in 1955. It covers all aspects of farming activities, including dairying and has a strong presence in Europe.

The **Irish Farmers Journal** is the voice of Irish farmers in print every week and voices the concerns of all farming activities including milk price comparisons. It is the largest farming newspaper in the country and has a wide readership even in urban centres.

The **Irish Farmers Monthly** was established in 1975, with a direct mail circulation of over 20,000 it reaches top farmers and key agri-business people. The magazine is aimed at the premier dairy, beef, tillage, and sheep farmers in the country, contractors and key agri/business people. As a monthly magazine the Irish Farmers Monthly has the opportunity to analyse key stories affecting Irish farmers while our key writers keep you informed, not just of agricultural issues, but also of European and international news.

For those readers who would like further information the following websites may be visited.
www.muintir.ie
www.macra.ie
www.ifa.ie
www.icmsa.ie
www.farmersjournal.ie
www.irishfarmersmonthly.com

After 115 years its farmers are still Going to the Creamery
Newtownsandes Co-op
Moyvane, Listowel, County Kerry

Newtownsandes Co-op was registered on the 11th March in 1895 by the Assistant Registrar for Ireland Daniel O'C. Miley. While virtually all creameries of that era are now derelict or have been taken over for other purposes, this creamery is a notable exception. It is a hive of activity, carefully managed and kept in pristine condition. Newtownsandes has an annual milk supply of 4.5 million gals (20 million litres).

About 45 of its 90 milk suppliers still deliver their milk to the creamery every day, with the other 45 opting for bulk tanker collection – this is unique in the Ireland of to day. A true operator of the Horace Plunkett principles, Newtownsandes has an annual turnover of €10,000,000 providing feeds, fertilisers and agricultural hardware providing a high quality personalised service. The co-op is conscious of its pivotalRole in the community, more important today than 115 years ago.

The present general manager, Michael Liston, is

one of the longest serving managers in the country being appointed in April 1967. With a strong balance sheet and paying top prices for milk Newtownsandes heads for 150 years with confidence.

Kilmeaden Creamery, County Waterford.

Local farmer, John McCarthy, going over Kilumney bridge, to the creamery, 1942.

5

The creamery suppliers

The creamery suppliers brought the milk to the creamery every morning for almost fifty weeks of the year. Allowing for variations in calving, the milk was taken in at creameries nearly every week of the year, with maybe only three days a week around Christmas. These milk suppliers came from a broad type of persons. From the couple of cows in the cottage acre to the two on the 'long acre' with a different section each day. The other end of the scale in the mid-50s would have been those with six twenty-gallon churns or some 120 gallons of milk each day and a variety in between.

Those that saw themselves as dairy farmers would have had between twenty and thirty cows and supplied some forty to sixty gallons per day. Most farms in the 50s were mixed farms with dairying and tillage – usually wheat, oats, barley and sugar beet if grown elsewhere in the area. They would also keep a few dry stock, mainly bullocks, which they would sell off at the local fair or in the new cattle marts that were springing up in many areas. The first of these included those founded by Ballyclough Co-op in 1959 and a few months later by Mitchelstown Co-op.

The average farm size in the 1950s would have been about forty acres but with many at the low side of 20 – 30 and a small number over 150 acres. The cows were mainly what was known as 'dual purpose'. These were cows that could give a reasonable milk yield (some 600-800 gallons) and would also give a reasonable return as a beef animal, and a butterfat average of about 3.4%. The most common breed was the Shorthorn, with a few British Friesians being brought in and always one or two Kerry Cows. Up to the 50s, most farmers used bulls running with the cows but from the mid-50s Artificial Insemination (AI) began to show its value in increased milk yields and higher butterfat tests.

The profile of the farmers varied depending on the area and the distance from the larger towns and cities. The highest percentage was married with children going to the local schools. Many of the small farmers also held down a job – if they could get one – in a local factory or often in the central creamery or co-op store. There were some farms with brothers and sisters who never married and lived under the same roof. These often lived in isolated areas of counties many in hilly areas and with long journeys to local towns. Then there were the two brothers living on their own sometimes one depending on the stronger one. In some cased one of the brothers might have had a slight disability, who could be 'put away' if the authorities found out. The more capable brothers were very loyal and often gave up the chance of marriage so that they could look after their sibling.

The last lot were the lone (and lonely) men who were left after the parents died and who had to wait until that happened to get ownership of the land. This was also the fate of lone daughters who looked after the old parents and finally got the farm maybe when she was 50+ with little prospect of marriage and certainly no likelihood of a family. Many of the 'lone rangers' lived in very isolated places. I recall many living in remote valleys of the Galtee mountains, often six to eight miles from the creamery and often with only cattle tracks to a local country road. The creamery was the only contact with other farmers and really provided a huge social input to their lives. These would have been very small suppliers – maybe six to nine gallons a day or less and once the creamery closed – that was a huge rift in their lives. Many of the 'maiden daughters' in their 50s were 'ripped off' by their labourers and in some cases worse, which in those days was kept secret. However, it is well to note that this was the exception but it did happen – like so much else that did occurred in those days and kept secret, much of which we are only now finding out about. Maura Cronin observed that

> There was a lot of bachelor farmers. They met no one on the farm and they had no contact with anyone until they'd go to the creamery. It was a bit of craic and sport going on. Whereas after the creamery closed they were on their own all day and they'd get depressed being all on their own on the farm. The creamery was good for them mentally and physically. It was an outing. I know you'd get drowned wet, but still they were out and meeting people, whereas when the creamery closed, they were kind of hermits on their own.

There were also the progressive suppliers who had a long-term view that milk would become a very important and valuable commodity in the future. They realised that high yields and butterfat, with low costs, could make their business very lucrative - many of these were co-op committee members. The most progressive farmer I saw was a supplier of liquid milk to Dublin Dairies and a man who grew up in the inner city. This man leased a farm of about fifty acres in the mid 60s and put fifty cows on it. Everybody was talking, but not to him. 'They' all reckoned on fast failure and took pleasure from commenting on the stupidity of people who had no farming experience. But the joke was on them! Not only did it work but he proved that with good management and proper animal nutrition even better results could be achieved on a cow/acre basis. Incidentally all his cows averaged 1,200 gals per lactation.

Distance from the creamery

Most branches were located so that the average distance for most suppliers was some two to five miles. This distance would be what some 60% of the suppliers travelled. The other forty varied with the longest probably eight miles and there were very few of these 'long hauls'. There were a variety of methods of transport, the two most common being the lowly donkey and cart, followed by the pony and cart. The mid 50s saw a handful of tractors and trailers and 'carry boxes'. The last named were usually Ferguson tractors with the 'box' mounted on the lifting gear with room for two or three churns. In the Dublin area, which was all for liquid milk, the delivery was by the dairy itself. HB and Merville had haulage trucks which collected milk from 'stands' outside the farmer's gate and took it to the dairy. All the collection was later standardised using ten gallon aluminium cans which suited the 'semi-automatic' system used by the dairies.

This system of haulier did also occur in parts of South West and West of Ireland with the creamery system run by the Dairy Disposal Company. The haulier system had much greater distances. The HB and Merville Dairies covered as much as fifty miles radius of Dublin. Likewise the travelling creameries operated in the southwest and west by the DDC also had a total distance of some fifty miles with four 'stops'.

The meeting place of the branch creamery in Ireland – and in many other countries - for close on one hundred years, was a huge social occasion which has never been analysed, researched or documented. (however, really good work has been started by a group at Mary Immaculate College, Limerick, led by Dr Maura Cronin). The closure of a creamery - very quickly and with nothing to replace it, was was a huge social upheaval for many - if not all of those suppliers described above.

The contact, the banter, the rivalry, the competition, the conversation, the business, the human aspects created a trend in Irish rural life - from which many parts of which have yet to recover - and it happened before. That time with the closure of the 'fair day' which were not as frequent an occurrence but look at the old photographs of the 'dealmaking' – the slap of the hand – the luck money – the parting of the animal he had reared. These were special moments taken with the progression of the 'modern' marketing system of the cattle marts and the impersonal auction system – one has to ask 'is it really better at the end of the day'? The market forces rule for better or worse.

Then there were the different characters. The busy progressive farmer would have left his churns on the platform with his passbook stuck in the lid of one churn. The empty churns would be picked up later in the morning by a neighbour, who would collect the skim milk. At the other end there was the last supplier - usually the same one and always one who lived near the creamery – he was entering the creamery gate when the last of the milk was literally flowing to the separator. In a few cases they were given a fright when a relief manager was doing the job and shut the platform doors and the farmer had to take the milk back home. Then there was the angry farmer, he often lived on his own because nobody could live with him. This type of individual was very intolerant of everything. If he was early there was somebody before him. If he was late there were others later. He would complain that he should have got more skim, that the storeman ignored him, that his milk had more butterfat, that the weather was too wet, that it was too fine and on and on and on. Everybody avoided him!

Then there was the feud. There is one story of two feuding farmers arriving towards the creamery gate together – neither would give way and speeded up their

Suppliers waiting at Barryroe 1940s or 1950s. *(Irish Examiner)*

horses, arriving at the gate together, crashed and turned both carts over spilling over 100 gallons of milk. One farmer suffered a broken wrist and one of the horses had to be 'put down' with the whole creamery intake disrupted, but the feud still went on regardless.

The characters were endless from the farm worker and his 'long acre' to the estate with 400 acres where the milk was brought by the 'farm manager' in the Mark 1 Land Rover.

Milk delivery vehicles

The milk was brought to the creamery in a huge variety of transport types – some of which have already been mentioned- from the ridiculous to the sublime. Probably the most common was the donkey with the pony a close second. The donkey was a favourite because of its docile nature and could be safely left – during the summer holidays – to the young family members, this was a great saving of a more important person during the busy hay and cropping season.

The pony could often be very sprightly and if not in strong capable hands could run, especially if frightened by a dog or other small animal and could knock the churns off the cart with disastrous results. Another no very common creamery nimal was the Jennet which was a cross between a female donkey and a horse; these could be quite docile or stone crazy and were kept by farmers who liked them.

Then in the late 40s and 50s the cars and vans started. In the beginning it would have been the Baby Ford with the wire wheels, with the back seat removed and one or two churns inside. Next came the Ford Prefect or Anglia towing a small trailer and the Ferguson tractor with the carry box, as previously mentioned. The Ford van and pickup were common around Cork where the Ford Factory was situated with the odd Austin A40 appearing with the bigger suppliers.

The scene was the same around the country even in the travelling creameries. I recall in North Clare having all donkeys and ponies all week but fancy cars on a Sunday. I was told that the cars were bought with 'merican 'money sent home by the relations.

Then there were the Hauliers, these were local men who would collect the farmers milk from a stand outside the farmer's gate on the roadside or from a designated collection point. These were uncommon in the main dairy areas but were common in parts of West Cork and in the Western Counties such as Mayo where distance to the creamery was a long way. The haulier used a small truck or more common a tractor and large trailer. In these areas the churns were usually the 10 gal types as the older 20 gal types were too heavy.

Maura Cronin in her 'Remembering the Creameries' sites- 'A haulier, he used to bring all the milk in a long trailer, used to bring up to a hundred cans of milk…. There would be a haulier in our area, now, bringing up to a hundred cans, and another haulier in Kilmaine and the far side of Ballinrobe – plenty of hauliers'.

Others saw status reflected in the modes of transport used – 'pony cars, ass and car and horse and car- all according to your station;

Variety of milk transport, John Sweeney and Ben Farrelly
wait in queue for Killeshandra Creamery.

Delivering milk at a creamery depot in the early 1930s.

'From these lines of carts it was often estimated what kind of farmers were there, how big they were and how efficient they were. One churn indicated a small farmer; two churns indicated a medium farmer and three or more meant he was a big farmer'.

'Mrs O'Brien she lived a mile and a half [from the creamery], about a mile we'd say. She used to bring two cans of milk in a trailer at the back of the bike. A small little trailer with two bicycle wheels on it and two tins of milk in it. Twenty gallons of milk, I think, she used to have in it, I don't know…' The adaptable donkey was the favoured mode of transport of women and smaller suppliers. 'Ah, there were a few women: Babe Casey with a donkey, Phil Seán Óg with a pony and Molly the Wood used to hitch a ride with her churn….over the road, from her own cross. Whoever'd come on first would take Molly, Molly and her churn over the road'.

But the donkey was more than this. He was the animal which young boys took to the creamery before the capacity to control a horse marked their initiation into manhood 'I took a donkey when I was about ten years old… Because I wouldn't be old enough for a horse. You'd want to be 14 to 15 before you'd be allowed a horse.

The creamery committee
The Co-op Committee was the final decision maker in the Society and its full title according to the general rules as laid down by the I.A.O.S. was the committee of management. The minimum number on a committee is ten persons as this is the

allowable quorum as laid down in the IAOS rules. The actual number of members is decided by the committee at its annual general meeting. The creamery committee had the real power in a co-op and it was they who appointed all senior persons including the manager. In some of the larger co-op's there was a small group formed e.g. the finance group which would make the day to day policy decisions with the manager. The other important officer was the secretary. In most cases this was also held by the manager. As Maura Cronin notes in *Remembering the Creameries*:

> *Within the ranks of the suppliers, too, there were definite lines of economic cleavage. Larger farmers tended to dominate the creamery committee, some families being represented on the committee over many years. At Kilmanagh in South Kilkenny, three generations of the same family might serve on the same committee and some individuals served for over half a century. But the committee did include middle-rank as well s big farmers, and it was much more than a power-brokering and decision-making body. It was something of a man's club which provided a monthly excuse for the farmers involved to escape the daily routine and return briefly to carefree atmosphere of their days as single men. Joe a farmer from Shannonside remembered it thus.*
>
> *Once a month the committee [met]. My father was a committee member. I can remember coming and meeting my father at the square in Askeaton and he'd be in the pub and he would call us in. He'd buy us sweets and he'd tell us to keep quiet, like, not to tell mother when we went home that he was in the pub. She'd be worried that he wouldn't come home or that something might happen to him. If he fell off the bicycle she'd have no one to milk the cows or look after the farm. We were young at the time, and a woman with small children and a lot of responsibilities, naturally had that worry that something was going to happen. They were a crowd of men together and they'd forget about their wives and children.*

In the larger co-ops the smaller top group wielded real power and sometimes liked to show it – especially in their dealings with banks. Many got concessions way over and above what was the norm in those because of their co-op position. The author can recall the case of the son of one of these boasting that he would get a good job in the co-op whether he did well at school or not - he did!!

A diverse group

Each creamery reflected the character and personality of its manager. There were some four groups of creamery manager.

Firstly, the managers of central creameries and in the time scale of the book there were some 174 centrals varying in size and complexity. In this group were the leaders and forward thinkers at a changing time in the dairy industry, changes in product range, in new technologies, in improvement of milk quality and quantity, finding new markets, etc.

The second group were the assistant managers. This group included the assistant general manager, the department heads and highly qualified technical persons in production, laboratories and quality control.

The third were the branch managers and also the managers of the independent auxiliary creameries. This latter group often had plumb jobs which were highly sought after, since they were autonomous co-ops supplying milk or cream to a larger co-op on a contract basis and guaranteed profitability with little problems. The ordinary branch jobs were the mainstay for creamery managers often allowing the managers scope to get involved in other activities.

The travelling creamery managers were usually done by young managers just qualified and getting valuable experience before moving on to a branch or other position.

When a central management position became vacant the method of appointment of a new manager was an important event. Once the advertisement was placed by the co-op, there was usually about one or two months for potential candidates to apply and to canvass the committee members. It was the committee members who made the decision at the designated meeting. It was usually a competition between up to five central managers in similar or slightly smaller co-ops and often the assistant manager(s) of the advertising co-op. It was very much like the Seanead elections with the candidates going from committee member to member hoping to win their votes at the selection meeting. It was all highly agri-political. If a manager was well known for some achievement, it gave him an important plus-factor. In the larger co-ops, the time-scale could go on for up to two months but usually not more. On rare occasions one or two of the candidates would be asked to make a presentation to the committee and the committee would then vote to select the desired candidate. In a few cases, the committee would have a desired person that they would contact directly but this was not common. In a small number of cases, the son replaced the father and very successfully but this was not often.

The characters stood out from these were from large medium and small central creameries and also from some Dairy Disposal centrals. Some stood out because the could see the value of publicity in winning new markets. Some were known because of their sporting prowess in GAA, rugby, and athletics or with horses, point- to -point or greyhounds.

The assistant managers and branch managers often settled down and married in their places of work. Many became very involved in their local communities thereby giving of their time and talents to their adopted areas.

Those in the Dairy Disposal groups of creameries stayed very much within the system, since being wholly owned by Government they had the status of civil servants with pension and other state 'perks' and were loathe to leave that special position. At times it became a contentious situation as many managers were by the mid 1950s trying to get their co-ops to fund pension rights with little success. This aspect was finally broken by the work of the Irish Creamery Managers' Association and their then general secretary, Captain D.J. Barry.

The phantom suppliers of Ballyahoo

Like all jobs there are certain 'cute hoors' who think that they have worked out the perfect 'scam' and of course the creamery system was no different. This is the alleged story of Mickie 'horse' Ryan who was manager of what was known as an Independent Auxiliary somewhere in Tipperary and related here as Ballybahoo.

Mickie was one of the ould school and got the job through succeeding his father Paddy 'co-op' who virtually started the creamery with the Chairman Tom 'the jockey' Ryan. Unfortunately Mickie was no son of his father, but then as an only child and son he was adored by his mother who died in a horse riding accident when he was 16 and then his father gave him everything and took him in to the creamery as his assistant after a year in the Albert College in Glasnevin, during which he learned all about girls, gambling and gin and having completed his apprenticeship in the father's creamery got one of the last of the Irish Creamery Managers' Certificate's –but no one really knows how.

It was then he really started living , bought a new car – a sporty MG - Mickie would take in the milk most days and once he was finished he left the rest to his father and was gone –to the races- Mallow, Limerick Junction, Listowel, Tralee. He'd often hit the dogs in Clonmel or Limerick a well, and the gambling increased. The mother had been well off from a wealthy farming family and he was left comfortable as one would say, but this was dwindling also. His father Paddy was getting on and did not know everything but was trying to ensure that Mickie would succeed him as manager. So he had a chat with Mickie and of course Mickie was no fool and assured the father of his desire to succeed and to work harder. All went well with Mickie only going to the horses only one day a week, at the next committee meeting the manager raised the question, having already discussed it with his friend Tom Ryan, 'the jockey approved and would support it, and so with little difficulty Mickie became Manager of Ballybahoo a real little jewel of an independent Auxiliary with some 80 suppliers and a guaranteed market for milk and cream and very little hassle. Mickie had a good life, he was 39 and had had gone out with a variety of women but did not appear to be interested in 'settling down' life was to short and to good, his Da was still keeping an eye on things and he got into the routine of the monthly accounts and returns and could handle them and still leaving time for his races and dogs.

Then a few days before Christmas he found is Da lying beside his bed – he was dead – he was 75 - never sick a day he got a massive heart attack and fell out of the bed trying to get to Mickie's room an old Frankie Lane tune going through his head – 'If the right won't get you then the left one will'

Paddy got a great send off with most of the suppliers present as well as all the creamery and store staff who considered him as their friend and helper as well as their boss.

Little changed for a while things went as before with Mickie's friend, Joe Mac, the store manager looking after things while Mickie was at the races. Joe was a kindred spirit, a relative of the chairman, Tom Ryan, and liked a flutter on the horses also, so Mickie would always have a bet on for Joe and he always had a few pounds winnings for Joe on the following day.

Then Mickie went to the Curragh races driving the new Mk2 Jaguar bought from part of the healthy legacy left by his father. Chatting to a trainer friend about prospects for the next race this gorgeous lady approached and so Mickie met Allison who was American and had lost her husband Chuck in a car accident the previous year. Chuck had been a builder and owned a couple of horses which had to be sold to complete his current contracts. So Allison was on a break from a difficult time and trying to pick up the pieces.

Mickie fell head over heels and the pair swiftly became inseparable. The co-op was going well so Mickie felt he needed a young manager to do the routine work, sign is on he hired Tommy Looney who had been working up the country and was interested in getting down south – or that was his story. An affable young man driving a Mini Cooper he made a hit with Mickie so he got the job and started on the platform the following Monday.

He fitted in well and it was not long until Mickie let him run the milk intake and the monthly accounts for the milk while Mickie looked after the new creamery farm they had recently bought and of course also Allison who was never far away.

And so life went on and Tommy was 'hail fellow well met' with the suppliers and staff, a year later coming back from a motor rally special section his Mini Cooper went off the road and into a bog. Tommy ended up in hospital with two broken legs and severe concussion so Mickie had to take over his work and as it was the end of the month the accounts also. Mickie took home the books and was working away. He had finished totting the platform books and then did a count to check that all were included the count was ten more than in his time; he knew that there were 6 new suppliers so he counted again – still ten over. Now he had to check each name against a master list which was locked in his own office safe with the co-op Share register. His heart skipped a beat as he discovered four phantoms!!

Nice little Tommy had been discovered, Mickie rang the chairman Tom Ryan and told him the facts continuing to ensure that the full extent would be known in the morning as he would work on until he discovered the total of the phantom payments. Tom thanked Mickie for his prompt call.

At 2am, Mickie had figured that Looney had skived about £2,000 from the Society, so he went to bed and figured on confronting Tommy in the hospital the following morning. So early the following day he phoned Tom Ryan who expressed a desire to accompany Mickie and they both travelled to the hospital arriving at about 11am, went to Tommy's room – it was empty, Checking with the nurses and matron they discovered the horrible truth Tommy had absconded. And so the Phantom Suppliers of Ballyahoo disappeared for ever. The outcome was that Mickie was lucky to have had a good win the following day so he decided to repay the £2,000 and give his personnel selection to professionals – he later discovered that Tommy had got £1,000 from the last job before doing the same. Mickie's uncle a Garda Super in Dublin later told him that Mickie was in the UK - Look out Express Dairies!!!

The Christmas Turkey Campaign – highlight of the winter

The Turkey Campaign started each year in early December. The basis was an excellent idea as at that time of the year the milk cheque was zero and with Christmas coming money was needed, particularly the farmer's wives. In addition with short supply of milk there was very little for the workers to do in the cheese and Butter so this campaign not only kept them busy but gave the opportunity for extra cash. With this in mind the 'Boss' Roche' found an export outlet for fresh Irish Turkeys on the London Smithfield Market in addition to Dublin and Cork. This market was of the order of 10,000 + birds delivered in crates 'dressed' weighed and ready for sale in the two weeks before Christmas.

This was a job that the farmer's wives took to their hearts and almost every milk supplier's wife reared from 10 to 150 or more turkeys for this market. I can well remember in my younger days on visiting my aunt's farm, the strutting turkey cock was an individual not to be messed with and better to avoid. These were the Bronze turkeys, little seen in the present times, and descended from the original North American bird. These birds, while not as good to put on weight quickly were much tastier and now will command a high premium – if you can find them. The use of turkeys for meat goes back for centuries

Rearing the turkeys

Mary O'Brien was getting the breakfast and her husband Tom came in from milking the cows and getting ready to go to the creamery. 'Tom, I think I'll get some extra turkeys this year, I could easily do another 40 or 50 and 'twould be a fair bit more money for the Christmas'. 'You sure 'twould not be too much,' replied Tom. 'I'll be ok,' Mary said, 'now that young Nora is going to school and anyway Elisha

Paddock reared turkeys.

113

and Anna are now big enough to help me in the evenings when they get home from school" "That's all right then" agreed Tom "You can use the bigger calf shed as most of the cows are not calving until the New Year".

It was late August on the O'Brien farm a short distance from Ballindangan Branch. Once the decision was made Mary started to prepare for the rearing of almost 150 turkeys which was quite a handful.

The large calf shed was fine but it needed cleaning and all the high openings to the outside had to be closed up with chicken wire and all the ground level openings

Free-range bronze turkeys.

sealed to prevent rodents, particularly rats entering as they really like young turkey poults for dinner-or breakfast!. A brooding area also needs to be prepared and this needs to be well insulated from draughts and rain and provided with the required feeders and heaters to ensure the correct rearing temperature and conditions. The heaters in those days were often oil burners using kerosene (paraffin oil as it was then known) as sometimes the sheds did not have electricity and the availability of the proper heater bulbs were often scarce and expensive.

The broad-breasted bronze birds were at this time the most common and did not begin to be replaced by the white variety until the later 60's. The bronze bird was more flavoursome but there was considerable evidence that there was better conversion with the white bird.

So when Mary O'Brien had her shed ready she approached the poultry adviser, who was employed by the County Committee of Agriculture, the advisory branch of the Dept of Agriculture to give her the information on day old poults and to check that all was ok in her preparations. There were a number of large commercial hatcheries in the Cork area; in fact a number of co-ops had provided this service for their own suppliers and also for other farmers in their catchment area.

In those days the common method of delivering day-old-chicks and poults was by bus. It was common to see a queue of farmer's wives awaiting the local bus to collect boxes of day-olds. They were delivered in special cardboard boxes which had a series of air holes and if one was travelling on the bus you certainly would be kept awake by the constant chirping on the journey.

The importance of the poultry industry especially turkeys is emphasised here quoting part of a Dail (parliament) debate on 13th November 1952. There are three speakers, Deputy Cogan, Deputy M.P. Murphy and the Minister of Agriculture, Deputy Walsh. Deputy Cogan said that

> *Yesterday the Minister announced that the price to be paid for well-finished turkeys in the Christmas Market this year will be 3/6 per lb. That is the price payable to the producer for live weight turkeys. While this price represents a reduction of 7d per lb on last years price and may bring a certain amount of satisfaction to the city housewife, it is a severe blow to those engaged in the production of turkeys. In the main, turkeys are raised by the womenfolk in rural Ireland as a means of supplementing their income and of providing the housewife and her daughters with a little money which they can call their own. It is only right to say that many of the most successful men in business and the professions owe their education to the hard-earned money derived from the poultry industry, particularly turkey rearing. It is not necessary to dwell on the grave risks encountered by the turkey raiser. From the moment the young turkey breaks the shell, it is menaced by every hazard. If not destroyed by rats in the early stages of life it may be killed by a heavy shower. If it escapes these risks and passed the red head stage, it may succumb to the disease known as black head. There is a variety of diseases to which turkeys are liable, various forms of diseases of the liver. Having escaped all these hazards, the turkey may be devoured by a fox.*

Deputy M.P.Murphy added:

> *As mentioned by Deputy Cogan, turkey raring is not that soft, money-making job that some people ,who have no knowledge of it, believe it to be. On the contrary, those people have to face many risks. First of all the mortality rate in young turkeys is much larger then among any other type of poultry.*

So Mary O'Brien purchased her poults from a trusted hatchery and started the first difficult seven weeks in the brooding area, first getting the day-olds to feed and drink water and then to watch the temperature and the security of the whole area. After seven weeks they were quite large birds and were left to use more of the shed to exercise and spread out. There was a constant watch to ensure that none had got sick as an infection would spread very quickly. Luckily the experience of the past years and the good care paid off with only two getting chills and dying, unfortunately another two stronger poults found a gap in a corner of the brooding area and were found as empty carcasses the following morning having been killed by rats who were constantly trying to break in.

As the days went by the turkeys became large birds and many had to have their wings clipped to stop them trying to fly out. They were fed on a sloppy mix of yellow meal and flake maize with many adding chopped nettles picked from the ditches which had traditionally been done by her mother also for hens. One other fine cock finally managed to break out one night, as was to be expected Mr Fox was watching and had an early Christmas dinner.

And so as the day approached for the Branch sale Mary had only lost 5 birds out of 120 poults a very satisfactory outcome indeed. On the day of the sale the birds which were fasting since the previous day were tied in pairs by the legs and packed in the large car trailer for transport to the Creamery. That year -1950- the price was unchanged at 4/- per lb and given an average weight of 12 lbs per bird Mary's cheque was a handsome £276. – a lot of money in 1950 – would even buy a new Ford car.

Turkey buying

When the buying started at the beginning of December, the milk from the cows had virtually dried up and there was only creamery one or at most two days per week at the branches. So the turkey buying at each branch was fixed for the days when no milk was being taken. The turkey team usually consisted of about five or six depending on the particular branch and their numbers of turkeys.

The Branch Creamery Manager was the boss and the key man of the team as his decision was final and he wrote out the cheque there and then for the turkeys. The 'second' most important was the turkey 'expert', who may have been a local, but more likely was from another area and who had experience of judging poultry, especially turkeys. His main job was ensuring that no 'auld' birds were bought at the top price and found their way into the export crates and also those with full 'craws' which would be paid for and emptied later..

The main method of checking entailed two clues, the first and best was the breast bone – if this was very pliable and gristly – the bird was young – if hard bone then the bird was an 'auld hen or cock. The other give-away were the wings and feet which could show age, although these methods were not as sure as the first.
The rest of the team comprised the local branch staff.

When the turkeys arrived they were brought in all sorts of transport – horses and carts, donkey and cart, tractors and trailers, cars, vans and even pony and trap. The big difference in the branch this time over normal times was the presence of women – so the men were watching their language! The birds were taken from the cart usually in pairs with their legs tied with 'binder twine', after checking by the expert they were placed in the weigh-pan of the milk scales in fours and sixes depending on size. The weight was recorded and the birds were taken to the post-weigh stall until all that lot was finished. When the final number was agreed with the producer, they were placed in the truck for transport to the Central and the cheque was written and handed over.

Everything would go grand until the 'expert' accused a seller – Jaas mam! This wan's a granny! Whereupon an argument would develop and go on and on only to be resolved through intervention of a few neighbours and a compromise: the local Manager kept out of the situation if at all possible.

The other common diversion was a young cock freeing his legs and taking off from the platform flying up to the rafters or the most inaccessible perch he could find. What developed then was initially an attempt to 'talk him down' followed by offers of the most succulent feed and finally a magnificent display of lassoing from local 'experts' in the best traditions of Gene Autry, Tom Mix or Ronald Regan – but to no avail: the young cock stared down and went 'gobble, gobble, gobble ' at various intervals. Left to his own endeavours he eventually wandered down to the other birds and was captured by a little old lady to the disgust of the 'cowhands'!

What with cheques being cashed in the local post office or shop the afternoon developed into a party atmosphere and the 'hot toddies' and pints were flying in the local pub well before the final birds were finished. The platform and scales were washed and made ready for milk on the following day, the team departed with the last load of birds for the Central, then all the local staff retired to the then well developed Christmas sing-song in the local.

'Feather Pluckers'

When the turkeys arrived from the Branches to the Central, they went to three large sheds, converted from lorry garages for the operation. These sheds adjoined each other with internal connecting doors and large doors to the outside yard. The arriving turkeys were put into one shed which was divided in two, where the cocks were put into one side and the hens on the other. As they were put in the leg ties were cut so that they were free to move about in their own section.

The second shed was the killing shed and had 4 or 6 long ropes hanging from the roof trusses. The turkey was taken from the first shed and its legs secured with the hanging rope. The turkey killer caught the bird's head in his hand, pressed down and twisted and the bird was dead. The deft killing routine was a learned skill and done correctly the bird was killed quickly and humanely, the bird was then handed into the plucking shed.

The plucking shed was unique and is probably the part of the campaign that stays most vivid in the memory. Picture a large shed about 50 feet square with planks placed on butter boxes around the three walls and providing seating for 60 – 80 pluckers. The pluckers usually came from the 'Queen Mary' which was the main cheese factory which was not working in the winter so these workers, both men and women were on short time and were delighted to make a few extra bob for the Christmas.

The 'crack' was mighty, the banter breezy and the competition was keen and exiting as each plucker came into the shed, signed on and took his or her place. The individual garb was interesting, with a variety of pullovers and jumpers under the white coats and wellingtons with two or three pairs of socks they were like a cross between Soumo wrestlers and American football players – all to keep out the cold and damp- and the fleas. The 'dressing 'of the turkey for the market was explained in detail by the 'inspectors' where certain feathers were removed or left on. The inspectors were the department managers in the central creamery and the cheese and butter departments which were shut or not busy at the time of year due to low milk and cream intakes. The standard uniform for the plucking house inspector was two or three white coats a long scarf and a cap, all to keep out the chill and the fleas.

The procedure was for the plucker to finish the bird, and then bring it to the table for inspection, the inspection consisted of a detailed examination of the plucking. At the beginning every bird had to be closely scrutinised as the pluckers had not plucked turkeys since the last Christmas and some had likely never plucked before. Prior to starting a sample of the correct finish was shown to all and the finer points were explained. This showed where certain feathers had to be left on or removed as the sample indicated. A sudden jerk when removing a feather could easily result in a tear which made the bird class 2. If passed they were credited with a point, if not right or damaged they had to correct the finish or place the bird on the damaged table. The inspectors' decision was final and initially they were very strict as the payment for plucking was by number plucked but the bird had to be perfect.

The visit of the 'Boss' one of the nights was always special. He would come in and greet everybody, wish them a happy Christmas and then the crates of porter and the rest would be brought in. This would usually happen on the last night when the finish would be done the following morning. The party would go on until the drink was gone – despite the fleas!

There were always the characters there was Sonny the fastest plucker in the west (shed) he really could pluck and average bird in less than 2 minutes and Biddy the fastest of the women and then there was Tommy –retired for years but always came for the turkeys, it would take him all night but the Boss Roche would always give him £20 for Christmas– the arguers who would try to short cut, the fast pluckers who would try to hide the short feathers on the legs

The turkey campaign was one mad rush and every year we would say 'never again' but the hype, the crack and the banter and the Christmas spirit made us forget fast and after a good soak in a hot disinfected bath – to get rid of any remaining 'visitors' we looked to Christmas and the New Year!

Travelling branch creamery

This was a unique machine developed by a brilliant young Creamery Manager John Blackwell in 1936. It was invented through need following the establishment of the Dairy Disposal Company as a means to take over and sell the remaining Proprietary Creameries following the increase in Co-op creameries The Travelling Creamery is apparently unique to the Irish Dairy industry and to the authors' knowledge a first worldwide. The machine was mounted on a 1949 E-Series Ford truck chassis, comprising a box body having a timber frame with two half doors, one on the drivers side back and the other on the offside front.

A milk separator was bolted to the chassis and driven by a special PTO shaft on the gearbox through a series of V-belts. In the initial designs the milk was separated

The only remaining Travelling Creamery at Dromcollogher Vintage Day 2010. (See skim return funnel on right). In the picture are Pat Normoyle, John Quain, J.J. O'Riordan, Jim Grogan and John Biggane.

The last surviving travelling creamery, stored in Charleville.

cold and worked well although there were difficulties in the winter months. The cream was collected in churns which were changed after each 'stop'. The suppliers' milk was weighed in a portable spring scales tank and then released into a tank on the floor, from this tank the milk went to the separator. The cream was collected as above and the skim via a small pump to a tank mounted under the roof to the front. This tank fed another tank scales where the skim milk was returned to the supplier

Travelling creamery in Kenmare 1938 Driver's name is Hanly. *(John N Murphy)*

and used to feed calves, pigs etc.

The author had the privilege of working on one of these travelling creameries in the mid '50's. At the time it was not seen as any such privilege but as a job for the summer months while waiting to get something better as a fixed branch manager with one of the bigger Co-op's. The one I worked in was in the North Clare Creameries in Ennistymon. I travelled from my home in Mitchelstown by train to Limerick and from there to Ennis. From Ennis I travelled to Ennistymon on the narrow gauge West Clare railway in a diesel railcar, this railway was made famous by Percy French with his non to flattering song, and was a fascinating experience.

This Central butter making creamery was newly built and was served by a number of branches and some seven travelling creamery routes. The route I was on had four 'stops' all at cross roads and all in all covering some 50 miles travel each day. Mauricesmlls, Kilnamona, Barefield, and Dysert The driver Mick Skerritt would pick me up from my 'digs' about 6.30 a.m. when we would head off. We had about 30 – 40 suppliers at each stop. Arriving at a stop we got the truck ready for operation. This entailed hanging out the reception scales and the skim scales fitting the milk intake funnel and getting the separator up to speed. The manager also had to get ready the box of Milk samples for that stop and the box of butter and platform book for writing in the amount of milk from each supplier. By the time all this was done the first suppliers were arriving and we started to take in the milk.

The amounts varied from five or six gallons up to 50 gallons at most stops with

Travelling creamery near Cahirciveen 1959 – John Hinde postcard. *(John N Murphy)*

an average of some ten gallons at each stop. As the suppliers queued up the separator was started, first with a quantity of water from one of the churns and the milk then turned on. As the milk hit the separator discs the sound changed and in a short time the cream flowed into the churn. One had to keep an eye on the cream later in the morning to ensure that the churn did not overflow so Mickey and I kept close watch.

The must common method of transport was a pony or donkey pulling a standard timber cart with wooden wheels and a steel rim. The farmers would travel a couple of miles to the stop each day including Sunday. Now Sunday was different and we usually started half an hour early. The other difference on Sunday was the mode of transport of the suppliers, even in those poor days of little income a great number would drive up in motor cars – many of relatively new vintage like Ford Prefects or Austin Cambridge's – Mickey later told me they were bought with

Ford truck model
used for travelling
Creameries in the
1950s.

Charleville
model milk
intake side.

Separator in travelling creamery.

' Merican money from relatives in the States. There was hardly a family in County Clare who did not have many relatives that immigrated during the famine period.

The big problem was a breakdown as this would put out the whole timetable and it was worse if it happened early. The most common of course was a puncture in one of the lorry tyres and this would require jacking up the lorry- no mean task and changing the wheel, this would only happen if it was a front tyre since the rear had twin wheels and a puncture would not stop us getting to the other stops and back to Ennistymon. There was of course very poor communication in those days one was lucky if there was a telephone in a small village and even if there was it may not work so one just did not try.

One of my colleagues that year Mick Whelton had a narrow escape one morning that summer. He was on one of the Northern routes towards Lisdoonvarna where there are some very tricky bends Stephen his driver was on the route for ten years but as they were coming back to Ennistymon on one of those bends a front tyre blew out, on top of that there was a soft shoulder which gave under the weight and over she went on her side and skidded through the hedge and sliding to a stop. Stephen and Mick were well shaken but OK and only one cream churn lost its lid and was only half full so the Boss O'Dwyer back at the Central would be pleased. When we got back from the run we had to write up the platform book into the Central ledger and total all the stops square up the butter boxes and fill out the daily reports. As we were then finished for the rest of the day we would walk the road to Lahinch and go for a swim.

The travelling creamery was a very important innovation in Irish rural life and provided a means of income to the farmers from milk at a level of expenditure which was economically acceptable at the time and proved a more practical solution than milk collection centres which were used in many European and other Developing economies. Having a number of year's experience in these developing countries I am of the opinion, that a modern version of the Travelling Creamery has an export potential under Europe Aid, World Bank and IMF and other similar programmes Two such areas in the Balkan states come to mind – Montenegro and Kosovo and also in parts of Africa.

The travelling creameries were operated by the Dairy Disposal Creameries in areas which had sparse and widely dispersed suppliers with relatively small quantities of milk and where it would be uneconomic to build and operate branch creameries. In addition to North Clare there was East Clare, West Clare, Coachford in County Cork, Terelton and West Cork Creameries. There is now only one such vehicle in the country and is owned and protected by Golden Vale, now a part of Kerry Creameries.

The summer in West Clare was idyllic and there were about eight of us all staying between two houses on the main street however we all had dinner together at Mrs Madigan's and the crack was mighty over the time of the meal. The weather was great and finishing our dinner we would often walk the three or four miles to Lahinch Strand for a swim or go the cinema and try to get talking to one or more of the young ladies now home from college for the summer holidays . Sometimes

Some of the original staff of Ballyclough Co-op.

we would swap routes unofficially in order to experience the different and beautiful countryside covered by the creameries. Sunday morning in Ballyvaughan was an experience never to be forgotten.

Relief branch manager

The relief branch manager was really a 'Jack of all trades' and was often the job given to newly qualified young managers. The relief came about for a variety of reasons the main one being holiday relief. It had been a rule that holidays could only be taken in the winter months, when milk supply was low but over the years the Irish Creamery Managers Association had kept up pressure on Creameries for summer holidays the same as other industries and finally succeeded in or about the mid 1950's.

At this time there were nine branches with Mitchelstown itself –called the Central – making up the tenth. The nine were Araglin, Ballindangan, Ballyhooly, Ballyporeen, Curragourm, Darragh, Glanworth, Kilbehenny and Knockadea. Two others were built in the 1950's Kilworth and Kildorrery, the latter replacing an original creamery built by Gates of the major baby food manufacturers Cow & Gate. The family lived near Kildorrery up to the 1960's.

These ten milk collection intakes serviced some 2500 farmers in three counties on a daily basis for some 50,000 gallons of milk during the peak. Each of these branches was different and had their own ways of doing things, had their own characters in the farmers and in the managers So when some morning a pink faced young chap in a new white coat appeared on the milk platform, one thing was certain –he would not get an easy ride. One had to learn the hard way – as in all walks of life – and if weakness is shown then you're in trouble.

Thus it was when I waited near the butter office at 7.30 for the lorry to collect me for my first day taking in the milk at Curragourm branch as the permanent manager had been ill and was in hospital. A few minutes later the dark Bedford lorry pulled up complete with 800 gal milk tank and some six or eight twenty gallon churns in the back. I opened the passenger door and was greeted by the driver - Maurice Carroll - 'hop in there now young lad and we'll have you out in plenty of time'. Replying 'thanks,' I settled down for the 20 minute drive to the branch with the summer sun shining and the churns rattling my apprehension melted away for the moment. Shortly we were turning into the branch yard and already there were about five farmer's carts waiting. Getting out I went up the steps of the platform and introduced myself to the three branch staff, the engine man, the skim man and the platform man all had many years of experience and I knew that I needed to rely on their judgement especially in the first few days.

With the main shaft running, the machinery was humming up to speed as the first churn clattered on to the steel topped platform and I watched as it was tipped into the weigh pan of the scales as the final churn was emptied I had the sample bottle and took a sample for the fat test, read the scales and entered it into the platform book and then into the farmer's passbook , calculated the skim back and was settling down to what would become a practiced routine after five or six were through I got a nod from the platform man and found a twenty gallon churn sliding over to me with the lid off. I took a look in and there was floating at the top of the milk a big black rat – drowned but awful. Picking up a strainer I removed the animal and placed it on the floor and said to the farmer. 'You better take that churn home'
He looked me straight in the eyes and replied, "hat's wrong now isn't it out?' I returned, 'well its not going into my tank that rat could be diseased or could have pissed in the milk, make it easy and put it back on the cart – the other two churns are OK'. 'This wouldn't happen if our real manager was here' came the reply

'I'm sorry but he's not and that milk could contaminate butter or cheese and that's my final word'. 'Well I'll take it but I'm reporting this to the boss,' he said, putting back the lid and pouring the other two churns into the scales and with that he stormed off'.

The rest of the morning went OK with many getting butter which was marked on the books and one or two ordering AI (Artificial Insemination) for cows early 'in heat' one farmer announcing it was urgent as he didn't spot the 'bitch' until last evening. Missing having the cow in calf at the optimum time could effect the lactation and the time of peak supply in the following year. With the last farmer's milk weighed the wash up started. The final platform jobs now had to be completed.

These included the totalling of the milk intake, the amount of cream sent to the central. The balancing of the butter stocks and the phoning in of the AI calls; sometimes the 'bull man' would arrive and take the calls. The final item was checking the store stocks with the store man, mainly animal feed of various types for cattle, pigs calve etc. By this time the driver would be ready to go and it was the drive back to the Central and time for lunch.

The situation was similar in all temporary or relief positions with the incident relating to the rat being related in different stories from different branches. Another such story related to an older farmer who had always insisted that his reading of the scales was always right and 2lbs more than anyone else. I had not known this until he ranted and raved, 'gimme me right weight you young little hoor" he shouted 'tis 122 not 120 are 'ou fekkin blind as well as tick!' I just spotted Ned the platform making signals and replied. 'Jas! You're right Sir. I'll correct that'. The farmer smiled and off he went – happy.

Another was when this well dressed farmer arrived one morning in a large tractor (not often seen in those days) and proceeded to pour in his milk, spotting a very discreet nod from the platform man I moved in and blocked the scales, then sniffed the milk – it was really bad very sour, and all six churns were similar (some 120 gallons). I stood my ground and said, 'this is not going in' picking up a lid and putting it on a churn. You'll have to take it home'. He looked at me hard and said 'Do you know who I am'. I replied "no and I don't care, that milk is not going to destroy the cream" I thought he was going to hit me but instead he threw the churns back on the trailer and revving the tractor roared out of the yard.

I turned to the platform man asked 'what was all that about?' 'That was the chairman of the co-op,' he replied. 'I think he just learned a lesson, but you might not be here tomorrow'. 'Oh! Shit,' was my answer – but I heard no more and completed my two weeks.

The confrontations mentioned here were common however there are a few situations which ended up not so lucky with young relief creamery managers. One ended up in the milk receiving tank having sent back four churns of sour milk, another had a nice pair of black eyes but the worse case I heard was a really bad bastard that kneecapped a young manager with a shotgun – I won't name the county but he got nine months for his sour milk and there were no TV's in prison in those days.

Day in the life of a creamery manager

After a quick breakfast –cereal and a cup of tea I waited for the truck to pick me up. The time was 7.00a.m. and the Darragh Branch was some 6 miles from the town. The May morning was good with a little sun showing and nice calm conditions. My Da had been collected half an hour earlier since his branch –Kilbehenny – was the biggest with over 300 suppliers. There was a beep outside the door to announce the arrival of the lorry, a dark blue Bedford petrol lorry with the 'Sailor' Meagher at the wheel. A story that he had worked in the British Merchant Navy gave him the name, but nobody ever got the full story and the 'Sailor 'wasn't telling.

With an 800 gallon milk tank in the rear with 10-20 Gal churns for cream, I jumped into the cab and with a grind of gear from the old 'crash' gearbox off we went, crossing the Funshion river at Ballerrriderrig, past the golf course and through the rolling foothills of the Galtees. It was a wake up drive on a summer morning. There was little said in the mornings each with their own thoughts unless there was a football match to discuss or some 'ska' to multiply and pass on. As we coasted down the final mile to the creamery we passed some early birds in pony's and carts making their way to the creamery. Arriving at the platform there were 'Good morning's' all around and the platform man swung the cream churns off the rear and put the boxes of butter over by the platform desk.

The long shaft was running and the 'thump, thump' of the National oil engine could be heard. The whine of the separators getting up to speed and the hiss of steam from the heaters were the everyday working sounds. The 'Sailor' pulled the truck around to the milk outlet pipe. The engine man was getting the cream churns down to the take-off from the cream cooler and the pasteuriser was flowing hot water – all was set to go!

Beside the creamery yard was the 'store' also part of the co-op where suppliers

Darragh! Discovered in an ICOS box of photos -
the author has relatives who own the big field on the top left.

could get all sorts of farm requirements, in the main, animal feeds, poultry feeds, pig feeds, fertiliser and a small selection of nails, nuts and bolts. Also stocked were spares for ploughs, hay and corn mowing machines, binder twine and sections for hay and corn cutting knives. Other items like cement and other building supplies could be ordered. The store was run by the storeman, the daily returns were taken to the central by the creamery manager. The purchases were charged to the suppliers number (Darragh 24 etc.)

The first few suppliers had arrived and the churns clanged on the steel plating of the platform, the lids were removed and the first whiff of good fresh milk was clear so it was tipped into the scales pan. The scales had two separate sides or pans and two outlets emptying into two different tanks. One tank was for cheese or processing milk and was only cooled and pumped to the storage tank high up in the building, from where it flows by gravity into the 800 gal tank on the lorry. The other tank fed the separators through the pasteuriser and after separating the cream was collected in the churns and the slim milk pumped to a tank in the high platform where the 'skim man' would return it to the farmers for calves or pigs.

This rhythm continued with farmer after farmer - cans on the platform, lids removed, a quick sniff, into the scales, sample taken, scales read, amount entered into platform book and farmer's passbook, skim amount calculated, butter entered if taken and then on to the next. The only variation occurred was when a suspected

Typical car used by 'bullmen' in the 1950s –but not this clean!

sour milk can arrived, A pint or so as poured into a bucket and the steam hose put into it , as the milk quickly heated to boiling if it curdled it was rejected and sent home. There was no comeback, the result of the heating was self-evident. The cause was usually no cooling or dirty or badly washed churns. A lesson was learned. This crude heating was replaced with the infamous alcohol gun in the late 50's and was equally effective, however there was always the stubborn farmer who insisted that his milk would be OK if it was boiled. His wish was granted with the expected result and he quickly learned that the alcohol gun was equally accurate and shot his appeal down.

When the cheese milk tank in the lorry was full with 800 gals. the 'sailor' took it back to the central and the cheese factory in the 'Queen Mary' and then returned to the branch.

In the spring of the year many farmers would order the 'bullman' when delivering the milk. This was of course the Artificial Insemination Technician who was operating in the area. This new service by the Co-op was aimed at improving the cow breed and particularly the quality and quantity of milk by using highly successful bulls and was proving very successful. The system was quite sophisti-cated the 'Bullman' carried sufficient 'straws' in a special insulated container to inseminate maybe 20 to 30 cows and were given the calls by radio-telephone direct to the car or directly by calling at the branch if they were passing. Driving 'Austin Devon' A40's at a high rate of 'knots' they became known as the 'Austin Bulls' and many is the story that emanates from the beginning of the service.

The most common – for those uninitiated or too young was this 'with little or no knowledge of the procedure the rural housewives only knew that a basin of hot water, soap and a towel were required and so. The Austin would sweep into the yard at the usual rate of knots. The young tech would jump out and knock on the door of the farmhouse which would be gingerly opened by the housewife.

Without any greeting she would point out 'the cow's in the middle shed I'll get the stuff' and disappear into the kitchen. Busying himself the 'bullman' got his kit and wellington boots and long apron. The farmer's wife arrived with the 'stuff' placed the basin, soap and towel on a bench and turned to go , looking back from about ten yards saying, 'you have everything now!' – and as an afterthought, 'and there's a nail on the wall there to hang your pants' she disappeared fast.

During the summer months a white cloud of dust on a country road would be taken as an 'Austin Bull' going to a farm. Amusing though it may be the fact is that the improvement in breeding stock through A.I. has helped the increase in milk yields which almost doubled in a short few years.

The farmers continued to arrive up to about 11am and there was still a good crowd in the creamery yard. Some were looking at a new tractor that one of the farmers had just got, another discussing the weekend sporting results and congrat-ulating young O'Brien who was the main scoring player in the junior hurling semi-final. A few were in the store getting calf and pig rations and looking at a new hay turning machine which was on show from the distributors.

When all the milk was in the platform book had to be totted to get the total milk intake for the day, the total cream was checked from the engine man and by checking the number of churns. The butter total was checked what was left in the boxes All the creamery documentation finished I went over to the store, to get the previous days sales from the storeman and a list of orders for various animal feeds and other items kept in stock and any special orders.

By this time the 'sailor' was back from the central having delivered his first load to the cheese factory and the tank was now filling with the second load. The cleaning and washing routine was being carried out in the lower part of the creamery with water flying everywhere and the separators being stripped and the many parts being placed in a special wash trough.

There was a supplier waiting for me when I returned from the store who wanted advice on what his son might do since he was doing his leaving cert in a few months. I told him I would bring the UCC list of courses with me the following morning. As he went off another approached and asked if I had the phone number of the milk experts in Moorepark I gave him the Dairy Research centre Moorepark switchboard number.

By now the 'sailor' had all the cream churns loaded and the milk loaded and we were pulling out of the yard when the 'engine man' ran up with a note shouting 'would you ever give this to Kevin O'Brien – there's a funny noise from one of the separators- it could be a bearing'. So off we went to the central, pulling into the Butter yard first with the cream. I got off here and gave in my returns for milk and cream at the office where all the branch returns were kept. Then I went home and had lunch, this finished I went to the store offices to hand in the store returns and the orders for the goods to be delivered on the next day or so.

When I finished here I walked down to the King Square offices and went up to the Branch Managers office on the top floor. It was a big chilly room with half a dozen large tables and chairs and a couple of old sofas. Jack Nash and Johnnie Casey were arguing about the finer points of a football match while Paddy O'Donoghue was busy checking some documents. It was quiet as the monthly accounts were finished I chatted to Nash and Casey for awhile.

There were two electric adding machines and one Facit electric calculator lying on one table – total help for doing the accounts at the end of the month. It was all brain power in those days! My day was finished I went home about 5pm and got ready for football practice. I recall about this time IBM opened a computer bureau in Shannon to do commercial accounts for companies. The first – total memory was 12,000 bytes and it took up four acres! (Now a simple hand calculator has more).

Commercial Cheesemaking in the early days

Cheese is sparsely referred to in early Irish literature which indicated its use as a general food commodity. However, there is very little descriptive information as to type of method of production. The earliest traceable references come from Aisling Mhic Chonglinne, described as a unique social picture of Ireland of the twelfth century. This aislig, or 'dream,' refers to a scholar poets travels throughout the province of Munster. The cheeses described in the text were

Tanach: described as a firm and comparatively dry cheese.

Maothal: was as a soft sweet cheese, probably similar to the soft cheeses in Europe and varieties such as Quaeso Blanco, which is coagulated using acid such as lemon juice or vinegar.

In 1948, the then Professor of Dairy Technology, Michael Ó Sé, wrote a paper for the *Journal of the Cork Historical and Archaeological Society* which pointed out numerous references to the names of cheeses in Irish literature but, only in rare cases is any detailed information. Professor Ó Sé's categorisation and description of native Irish cheese taken from the Gaelic literature are here given.

Pressed cheeses

Cais: a word on loan from the Latin caesus and also the modern Irish word for cheese Ó Se suggests this term was applied widely to all types of cheese, but when used alone without qualification in the text, means pressed cheese.

Tanach: a hard pressed cheese made from skimmed milk and indications from the literature suggest it was pressed in small moulds.

Grus: classed often with Tanach, was probably a similar hard pressed cheese.

Faiscre Grotha: literally ' a compression of curds,' it can be assumed to be a curd cheese which had been pressed in some type of mould to give it shape and solidity.

Unpressed cheeses

Gruth: this is also the word in modern Irish for curd of any type.

That: a cheese made from sour milk curds, probably heated and stirred until they became plastic and cohered into a single mass.

Millsen: this appears to have been a sweet curd cheese or junket, made from sweet (fresh) milk.

Maothal: probably had a smooth texture and a soft body and is the cheese referred to in the vision of Mac Conglinne

Mulchan: a cheese that was made from buttermilk and referred to in a tract about 1500. Indications are that it was made until relatively recent times.

Professor Ó Sé concluded that the reason for the disappearance of these traditional Irish cheeses is connected with the political history of Ireland – 'cheesemaking being one of the many areas of Gaelic civilisation which was lost in the economic degradation of the Irish people subsequent to the English conquests of the 16th and 17th centuries'.

In the 17th and 18th centuries, there were very few references to cheese products. Those mentioned referred to Bonny Clabbar. or the curds in very sour milk. Arthur Young's *'Tour of Ireland'* published in the 1770s, referred to specialised dairies having cheese. However there were likely some of the 'big estates, which had imported English or Welsh cheese expertise'.

In real terms there was no production of cheese in Ireland in the 19th century, the combination of cattle and butter production continued with calf rearing benefiting from the skim milk produced during buttermaking.

The beginning of the 20th century saw the establishment of the Department of Agriculture and Technical Instruction, under the guidance of Sir Horace Plunkett. The early 20th century also marked the beginnings of the co-operative movement (which Plunkett founded) and the first creameries. Following a series of experiments on cheesemaking in Liscarroll and Ballyhaise, cheese was re-introduced to Ireland, the first variety being a Welsh type – Caerphilly – a pressed semi-hard cheese with Cheddar coming a few years later.

6

Cheesemaking in 'The Queen Mary'

The cheese department in Mitchelstown started in 1932 making the natural cheeses Cheddar, Caerphilly and Emmental cheeses. While some natural cheese was sold in Dublin and Cork and in some of the top hotels the mainstay of the cheese department was the processed cheese. Made from mixes of the natural cheeses and packaged in the traditional foil wrapped triangles as 'Whitethorn,' 'Galtee' and 'Three Counties' these processed cheeses put Mitchelstown firmly on the market as the 'Irish Cheese' and like 'Cadbury Chocolate' became the taste of Irish cheese. These three were very popular and were sold throughout the country and subsequently exported to many countries.

The mainstay of natural cheese production frem the 1940s was the building on the Clonmel Road known as 'The Queen Mary' mainly because of the series of extractor fans on the roof being like the funnels on a ship. At this time it held some 400 cheese vats each holding 400 gallons of milk. In those days' cheddar cheeses was made in these vats and during the process were stirred by hand continuously for 4 or more hours. The cheeses were made in 28 or 56lb rolls of red or white Cheddar. Emmental was made in special vats but not every day and were finished into large 'wheels' of about 180 to 200lbs, very large and heavy cheeses. This was a 'Swiss' type cheese and required different methods and special storage conditions. The 'Caerphilly' cheese was a Welsh type also made in the 400 gallon vats. In the late 1950s and early 60s many more natural cheeses were introduced by the new Cheese expert, John McCarthy, who revolutionised the cheese factory layout and built a new climate controlled cheese store. These new cheeses were introduced in order to create new varieties of processed cheese and also to increase the range of natural cheeses available for the increased interest in new natural cheese varieties mainly due to an increasing number of Irish going on foreign holidays. These new cheeses were Gouda, Edam, Dutch types and Danish cheeses like Samso and Danbo.

These were additional cheeses into an already busy schedule but through the new layout and thanks to the highly professional team of cheesemakers in the factory – head cheesemaker being Mollie Gallagher from Donegal – every new cheese type was successfully integrated.

At this time, all cheesemakers and buttermakers were trained at the Munster Institute at the Model Farm Road in Cork. In addition to the new cheeses, Mac (John McCarthy) introduced a new system for bulk starter production which increased the effectiveness of the starter and reduced the risk of starter difficulties

The cheese factory on the Clonmel Road, when Mitchelstown became famous as 'The Home of Good Cheese'. The cheese plant was affectionately known as 'The Queen Mary'. In the immediate foreground are the special wooden vats for making the large 'wheels' of Emmental cheese, each weighing over 100lbs. On the far left are the rows of 500 gallon vats for Cheddar etc. and on the far right a group of women sewing cheese cloths. William D. Hayes, assistant manager, is in the foreground.

(Bill Power Collection)

due to Phage attack (a starter disease). The old cheese stores were very extensive and held hundreds of tons of cheddar cheese and Emmental at various levels of maturing. The cheese was cleaned and turned on a monthly basis. The Emmental was first put into special warm rooms for a four to five week period shortly after being made in order to develop the traditional 'eyes' and the distinctive sweet nutty flavour and taste due to the specialised starter used in this cheese.

The turning of cheese on the shelves of the store was an ongoing operation as when the mature cheese went to the market or process it was continuously replaced by young cheese from the cheese factory. As each new cheese was prepared for the store it was stamped with number which related to the month, the day and the vat number, this meant that the history of the cheese could be traced back to the way that cheese behaved while being made in a very similar way to wine making.

The cheese for market and for processing was selected on a weekly basis. This selection was done by one or more of the cheesemakers or managers using a cheese borer which removed a plug from the block. The smell, texture and taste were the main criteria and being a good cheese selector required years of practice. For process cheese, such as 'Galtee' or 'Calvita,' there were different ages of cheddar required, depending on a strong or mild taste. For market and export sales to the London market the buyer often sent his own selector. These buyers would buy hundreds of tons at a time if the quality and maturity were what they wanted and Mitchelstown cheddar was consistently of this high quality. Winter stocktaking of

Pressing cheddar cheese and cleaning prior to putting on final cloths for ripening.
(Bill Power Collection)

all the cheese was required for the yearly audit and accounting and was a cold and tedious job during invariably cold and inclement weather with the wind blowing in from the Galtee Mountains. Each cheese had to be removed from the shelf, weighed, recorded and replaced on the shelf. This operation could amount to more than 100,000 (some 2,000 tons) in any one year at various levels of maturing.

Larger automated cheese vats were introduced in the late 50s and a new climate controlled cheese store was built. In the 1960s and 70s, further advances were made with automated cheese plants for Edam and Cheddar being built and bringing higher efficiencies and outputs for better profitability.

Creameries Manufacturing Cheese in 1956

Ballyagran Co-op Creamery Ltd, Ballyagran, Clarleville, Co.Limerick.
    Telegrams - 'Creamery Ballyagran'.
    Telephone - Ballyagran No. 2.

Baryroe Co-op Creamery Ltd, Lislevane, Timoleague Co.Cork.
    Telegrams - 'Creamery Lisalane, Cork'.
    Telephone - Lisalane No. 2.

Drombanna Co-op Creamery Ltd., Four Elms, near Limerick.
    Telegrams - 'Drombanna Creamery Limerick'.
    Telephone - Ballysimon No. 3.

Dungarvan Co-op Creamery Ltd., Co. Waterford.
    Telegrams - 'Co-operative Dungarvan'.
    Telephone - Dungarvan No. 3.

Effin Co-op Creamery Ltd., Newpark, Kilmallock, Co Limerick.
    Telegrams - 'Creamery Newpark Kilmallock'.
    Telephone - Charleville No. 9.

Experimental College Cork University.Creamery,
    Telephone - Cork No. 1201.

Freemount Co-op Creamery Ltd., Freemount, Charleville, Co Cork.
    Telegrams - 'Dairy Freemount'.
    Telephone - Freemount No. 3.

Feenagh Co-op Creamery Ltd., Charleville, Co Limerick.
    Telegrams - 'Creamery Feenagh'.
    Telephone - Feenagh No 2.

Glin Co-op Creamery Ltd., Glin Co. Limerick.
    Telegrams - 'Creamery Glin'.
    Telephone - Glin No. 6.

Herbertstown Co-op CreameryLtd, Knocklong, Co Limerick.
    Telegrams - 'Creamery Herbertstown'.
    Telephone - Herbertstown No 2.

Kantogher Co-op Creamery Ltd., Killeedy, Ballagh, Clarleville, Co Limerick.
    Telegrams - 'Ballagh Creamery, Charleville'.
    Telephone - Ballagh No 3.

Kilmallock Co-op Creamery Ltd., Kilmallock, Co Limerick.
    Telegrams – 'Co-op Cremery, Kilmallock'.

Mitchelstown Co-op Creameries Ltd., Mitchelstown, Co Cork.
    Telegrams - 'Creamery Mitchelstown'.
    Telephone Mitchelstown No 6.

Milford Co-op Creamery Ltd., Milford, Charleville, Co Cork.
    Telegrams - 'Creamery Milford, Cork'.
    Telephone - Milford No 3.

Newmarket Co-op Creameries Ltd.,, Newmarket, Co Cork.
    Telegrams - 'Creamery Newmarket, Cork'.
    Telephone - Newmarket No 5.

Rathmore Creamery, Rathmore, Co Kerry.
    Telegrams - 'Creamery, Rathmore'.
    Telephone - Rathmore No 3.

Shandrum Co-op Creamery Ltd., Newtownshandrum, Charleville, Co Cork.
    Telegrams - 'Creamery Newtown Cork'.
    Telephone - Newtown No 3.

Above: 'Three Counties' label from the 1930s.
Below: filling 'Three Counties' triangles made at the Kingston Process. *(Bill Power Collection)*

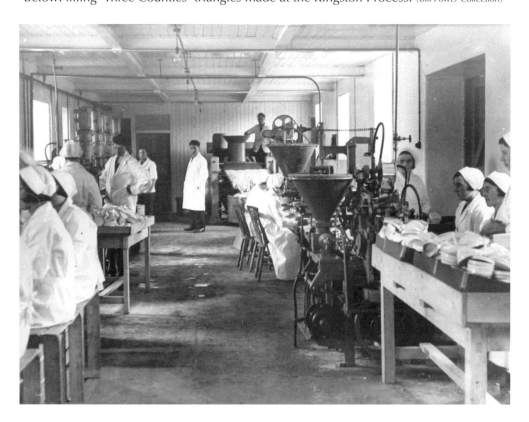

Processed cheese

The processed cheese factory at that opened at Mitchelstown in 1932 was the first Ireland and obtained an exclusive licence through the close friendship between Eamonn Roche and the then Taoiseach, Eamonn De Valera. The process factory was housed in the old stable buildings at the back of the creamery offices at King Square which had been the Kingston Arms Hotel and which we knew as 'Kingstons'.

The manufacture of processed cheese was straightforward and consisted of five operations;

1. Preparing the natural cheese, removing the rind, and removing any small cracks or blemishes.
2. Weighing the amount of each cheese type in the mix and feeding it to the blending rollers.
3. Setting up the final mix for the kettle.
4. Pasteurising the mix and pouring it into the Packaging machine.
5. Packing the Cheese in foil, and card boxes.

The Mitchelstown owned 'Galtee,' 'Three Counties' and 'Whitethorn' were the

Filling the 5lb boxes of 'Galtee'.
(Bill Power Collection

brands of cheese best known in Ireland in the 1940s, 50s and 60s, having been joined by 'Calvita' in 1940. This processed cheese was designed as a light tasting cheese and was intended as a brand that would entice children's appetites and would therefore be used by them in school lunches and as a home snack. It proved very successful and became one of the best known processed cheese products.

Natural unprocessed cheese had little place in the Irish diet at that time. The taste of processed cheese became a part of growing up as much as Cadbury's chocolate. In contrast to the natural cheese factory, almost all the employees in the 'process' were females. It was also a much cleaner and drier job. As production and the range of products increased, the old plant became too small. A new factory was built on Clonmel Road and this new facility introduced modern production methods and was equipped to manufacture the newer more complex products.

Work in the natural cheese factory

The day started about 7.30am with the early crew arriving to set up the vats, checking that there was no water in any, that all valves were shut, all stirrers in place etc. By 8am, the main staff had arrived and immediately went to the cheese presses

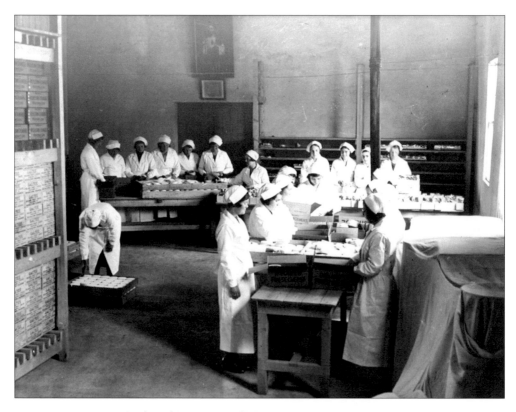

Final packing- note religious picture in top centre.
(Bill Power Collection)

Original cheese vats about 1933 at Clonmel Road above.
(Bill Power Collection)

and removed the pressed cheddar, took off the loose cloths, trimmed the edges and put on the stocking cloth and end pieces and folded over the edges of the stocking for maturing storage. If Gruyere cheese had been made there was a different procedure. The large wheels of Gruyere were removed from the special wide presses and the ropes on the moulds were untied to reveal the large 45-55kg (100-110lbs) wheel which took a man to lift or up to two women. Once removed from the press these large cheeses were kept on the board and slid off it into a brine bath for two to three days. After salting, they were removed onto a board and placed in a warm room for three to six weeks to develop the 'eyes,' after which they were placed in traditional cheese store for up to twelve months.

The staffing in the factory with 400 vats was about three per vat - one man and two women so there were some 800 to 1,000 working in the cheese at the peak of production in May, June and July. Employees came from rural and urban backgrounds. Just after 8am, the first of the trucks arrived from the branches with their 800 gallon tanks full. This would fill two vats directly through hoses and pipes by gravity. Once the vats were half full, the steam was turned on in the jacket and the stirrer started. For those vats with no stirrer one of the women would stir using a long wooden rake. This helped to get the temperature up on the milk quickly ready to add the Starter. Once the first vat was filled the second was started, sometimes the flow was split and both were filled together. Once the temperature was up to 30 degrees centigrade the starter was added from a special can. The bulk starter was brought in from a special room to ensure that there was no contamination. The vat was stirred for about 30 minutes and then retested for acidity to see if it was at the correct level for rennetting (0.20%) The rennet was kept in a large 10 litre glass container (called a carboy) and was an enzyme which coagulated the milk and came from the fourth stomach of a calf (now produced using biotechnology). This is very concentrated and is added at about 1ml per gallon of milk, or about a pint per vat diluted with water about 20 times and added to the milk while continuing to stir. If the cheese needs to be coloured, the colouring is now added. This is called Annatto and is very concentrated. Colouring spilled on ones hand will take two to three days to wash off.

The five cheesemakers had arrived before 8am and each was supervising a section of some 80 vats and had to do all the acidity and temperatures and get the lab to do any other tests required such as fat % of the milk depending on the cheese type being made. They were busy ladies. There were a large number of natural cheeses being made at this time some for new flavours in processed cheese spreads and also for sale as a wider range of natural cheeses. John McCarthy was the powerhouse behind the movement into higher milk quality, new cheese varieties and new innovations in the manufacturing process. I was his 'gofor'.

In the late fifties, we were making some nine different natural cheeses with Mollie Gallagher as head cheesemaker. Sho complemented the genius of John McCarthy. The main variety was Cheddar in both white and red, and in two sizes of finished cheese 28lb and 56lb, cloth wrapped in the traditional manner. Then there was its first cousin, Cheshire, which is very similar but not quite as hard but more crumbly and with a more acid flavour mainly in 28lb rolls. One of the oldest made in the factory since 1933 was Emental - a Swiss type cheese - finished in a large wheel like cheese and weighing over 90lbs. This was a sophisticated cheese requiring specialist starter and storage conditions and with a very distinctive flavour. The smaller cheeses were all of continental varieties with one exception – Caerphilly. This Welsh cheese was the first to be made in the modern redevelopment of cheesemaking in the early 20th century. Finished at about 15-20lbs, it is a semi-hard cheese with a nutty flavour and was popular with Irish workers as it was with Welsh miners in its original life in Wales. It was a big export from the English proprietary creameries during the First World War for the British Army.

The two main continental types were Gouda and Edam – originated in the Netherlands were semi-hard with Edam having reduced fat content and finished in the traditional red wax and its ball like appearance. The final two were Samsoe and Danbo which both originated from traditional Danish cheeses that were used to give special flavours in new processed cheese types.

Cheddar and Caerphilly were the first cheeses made in Mitchelstown. This was in 1933. Cheese had not been a large part of the Irish diet for many hundreds of years since the farmers were driven off the land in the 16th and 17th centuries and

2,000 gallon cheese vat with overhead carriage in late 1950s.
(Bill Power Collection)

it was given to English landlords. Even the dairymen who made butter for the butter markets did not have cheesemaking skills and during all this time (17-18th centuries) cheese was only made in a few of the large English-owned estates for their own use. Cheese had been an important part of the Irish diet going back to references in the 'Annals of the Four Masters' and later in references to Saint Patrick. The restart of cheesemaking was begun about 1900 with the setting up of the Department of Agriculture and Technical Instruction and the carrying out of experiments in Liscarroll and later in Ballyhaise. This continued until about 1910, with the first phase of a milestone in the development of the modern dairy industry when commercial cheese was made in County Tipperary and County Waterford around 1912 and the number grew to nearly 200 by 1918 when some 7,000 tons was produced, all cheddar or Caerphilly this continued and doubled again in 1919.

The first cheese vats of the day had now reached 30 degrees centigrade and the Starter had been added. This starter or culture was (and is) a key element in the cheesemaking process and the differences in cheeses are in most cases related to the culture used. The preparation of the bulk starter is a very sophisticated and exact operation as it can get infected by other strains of bacteria and worse by a 'phage' which is a virus type organism and can render the starter useless. Hygiene and cleanliness is paramount as in a very rigid operating procedure. A new system introduced by John McCarthy in the mid 1950s proved very effective.

Curd being cut into blocks for Cheddaring, Galway Bay Cheese Co. Tuam, Co Galway.

The acidity was checked by the cheesemaker after 30 minutes and if it had reached 0.20% acidity the rennet was added, diluted in a bucket of cold water and spread along the length of the vat. The stirrer was left on for about five minutes and then removed for the milk to coagulate. After some 20-30 minutes, the vat was checked to see if the curd was firm enough for cutting. The curd was cut using special knives made up of a stainless steel frame and strung like a harp with s/s wires spaced about half-an-inch. There were two knives a Vertical and a Horizontal and they were moved up and down the vat covering half the vat width on each run. Then across from one end to the other, this will cut the curd into half-inch cubes.

As the curd is cut the green whey separates out and as soon as the final cutting is done the stirrer was put back in and started to prevent the curd sinking to the bottom of the vat. As soon as the stirrer is working the steam is turned on and the cooking process begins. Different cheese types have different cooking temperatures and different methods of raising the temperature of the curd and holding it for specific periods [Also curd cutting methods] this is the process which distinguishes one cheese type from another. The cutting of the curd in the early 50s and before was manual and done by two men and took some 15 – 20 minutes per vat. This was a tough job with plenty of back strain for good measure.

When the cutting was finished the curd particles would sink to the bottom of

Later stage of cheddaring above.

the vat and the whey was on top. It is essential not to leave the curd knit together ay this time as it has to be cooked very slowly to a higher temperature. In the early days the stirring was done by hand using a wooden rake. When making cheddar cheese – which was the most common – the stirring continued for 40 minutes or more especially if the starter/culture was slow could take more than an hour. During this time the cheesemaker was taking periodic samples of the whey and doing acidity tests on it. This was a simple chemical test which was done at the cheesemakers 'station' on the factory floor.

Each test was recorded in the 'make sheet' for the day and each vat had a separate line across the page This record was important as the cheese which came from the particular vat could be traced right up to the date of sale and the final quality score it had reached.

When the correct temperature was reached the whey was released through a valve and strainer to prevent any curds escaping. The whey went to a storage tank and after separating to remove any fat left as whey cream, was fed to pigs on the creamery farm as it had a high sugar value.

As the whey ran off the curd sank to the bottom of the vat and a drain channel was cut in the centre. Then the curd was cut into large blocks and continued to drain The blocks were turned over about every fifteen minutes and the acidity rose and the acidity checked until it reached the required level for the cheese being made.

This turning was also a tough job as one was leaning over the side of the vat and turning the 4kg blocks of curd. This turning continued and when the acidity level was reached they were 'milled 'or chopped up into about 1 inch pieces. It was then salted and the salt mixed in with big forks and finally filled into metal moulds. These moulds were lined with cheese cloth and when full were placed in a vertical cheese press which pressed out the excess whey. The moulds were left for about an hour and then redressed and put back in the press – screwed up tight and 50lb weights hung on the presses until the following morning. In 1956 these presses were changed to horizontal –made in the creamery engineering shop – and fitted with air pressure and the moulds made of stainless steel, the same amount of curd was weighed into each mould. The first mechanical vats were introduced with stirring and curd cutting equipment making the work easier and the cheese of higher quality. The day finished for most at about 6pm but for those doing heavy washing and cleaning went on until about 8pm

Packing 56lb boxes.

Buttermaking in a West Cork creamery in the 1940s. (Irish Examiner)

Buttermaking in the Central

The Buttermaking department was on Clonmel Road and had been rebuilt and fitted out with new churns and cream cooling vats about the early 1950's so it was the newest and most modern of all the manufacturing plants. The cream came in 20 gallon churns from the branches and was weighed and pumped to the cooling vats to get the cream to the correct temperature for churning . When the vat was full – about 500 gals it was tested for fat % and if it was within 2% of 40 % fat it was OK, if higher some milk was added to lower it to the correct figure or add 50%fat cream to bring it up (this was not often). The churns at this time were the large timber ones usually of Danish manufacture and would churn about 500 gallons at a time and produced about 2240lbs of butter.

This was washed and worked in the churn and came out ready fro packaging into 56lb timber butter boxes or went direct to the Benhill roll wrapping machine which produced 1lb parchment wrapped butter for retail sale. A small number of 28 lb boxes were done for special orders. There was a standard marking on each Butterbox which was laid down by regulation. Tommy Keogh was the he buttermaker and followed his father Paddy who had been the first buttermaker in the Co-op. I recall one of the packers whose English was unique. He was going to England one Christmas to his son who was married and was asked at the customs for the Innisfallon boat to Swansea 'what's in that bag,' by the Custom officer. He

FEENAGH

Co-operative Dairy Society, Ltd.

FEENAGH, CHARLEVILLE

Guaranteed Absolutely Pure

Made from Pasteurized Sweet Cream
on Scientific Principles

FEENAGH, CHARLEVILLE

Co-operative Dairy Society, Ltd.

FEENAGH

IRISH
CREAMERY BUTTER

Reg. No. C204. 1-lb. Nett

ÉIRE
Irish Creamery Butter

ASKEATON

Co-operative Agricultural & Dairy Society Ltd.
ASKEATON, CO. LIMERICK,
'Phone No. ASKEATON, 4

Winners of numerous Prizes and Gold Medals.

Ask your grocer for "ASKEATON" Butter
PRODUCE OF REPUBLIC OF IRELAND.

Reg. No. 319   1-Lb. NET.

ÉIRE
Irish Creamery Butter

FROM
WEST CORK CREAMERIES
(DAIRY DISPOSAL CO. LTD.)
AUGHADOWN, Co. Cork.

Reg. No. C168.   1-lb. Net

ÉIRE
IRISH CREAMERY
BUTTER

Maid of Ibane

1-LB. NETT.

Produce of the
REPUBLIC OF IRELAND
GUARANTEED PURE
Made from Pasteurised Sweet Cream

From   **BOHERBUE**
Co-op Agricultural & Dairy Society, Ltd.
CO. CORK.
REG. NO. C313.

IRISH CREAMERY BUTTER

North Clare

CREAMERIES, ENNISTYMON

TELEPHONE: ENNISTYMON 8
TELEGRAMS: CREAMERY, ENNISTYMON

BORRISOLEIGH CELEBRATED "Golden Valley" IRISH CREAMERY BUTTER

SUPER QUALITY –IRISH– CENTRIFUGAL CREAMERY

DUBLIN 1963, 2 FIRST PRIZES
60 FIRST PRIZES AND 80 OTHER AWARDS

ARDAGH CREAMERY

ARDAGH, Co. Limerick

TRADE MARK CMD CASTLEMAHON
Reg. No. C 158
CHOICEST IRISH
Creamery Butter
GUARANTEED PURE AND UNTOUCHED BY HAND
1 LB. NETT
CASTLEMAHON
CO-OPERATIVE DAIRY SOCIETY LTD. CO. LIMERICK
PRODUCE OF THE REPUBLIC OF IRELAND

London, 1892 First Prize		Cork, 1931 2 First Prizes
Dublin, 1895 First Prize	Dublin 1950 : First Prize	Cork, 1935 First Prize
Limerick, 1896 First Prize	Dublin 1951 : 2 First Prizes	Cork, 1937 3 First Prizes
Tipperary, 1920 2 First Prizes		Belfast, 1937 & 1938 First Prize
Belfast, 1928 2 First Prizes		Cork 1939 First Prize
Dublin, 1928 6 First Prizes		Read Cup, 1942
London, 1928 2 First Prizes	Dublin 1955 : First Prize	Read Cup, 1943
	Dublin 1956 : 2 First Prizes	Read Cup, 1944
	Dublin 1957 : 3 First Prizes	Read Cup, 1948

REG. NO. C 109
IRELAND
Irish Creamery Butter

1 LB. NETT

REG. NO. C116
¼ LB. NETT
BRAND
Kilcrea

IRISH CREAMERY BUTTER
KILCREA
BRAND
Muskerry & Lissarda Co-op. Creameries Ltd.
FARNANES, Co. CORK.

MILD   MILD

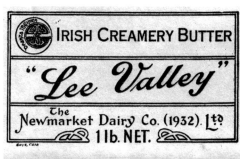

IRISH CREAMERY BUTTER
"Lee Valley"
The Newmarket Dairy Co. (1932). Ltd
1 lb. NET.

"Lee Valley"
MILD

Reg. No. C365   454 G   1 LB. NETT.
TELEPHONE:- "CAHERCIVEEN 7"
Caherciveen Creamery
ÉIRE IRISH CREAMERY BUTTER
SHIPPERS OF THICK RICH CREAM   ROLL BUTTER A SPECIALITY   TRADE

CREAMERY   IRISH   BUTTER
CAPPAMORE
CO-OP AGRICULTURAL & DAIRY SOC. LTD.
CAPPAMORE, Co. LIMERICK.

replied, 'a Jas Sir. There's nattin in dat only childeses clotheses'. Another time during the winter months they were asked to paint the roof tresses and when asked about the job replied ' ah! Jas that effin job 'ed masecrate ye'. As time went on the timber churns were replaced with cubic stainless steel ones and finally to the automatic Buttermaking machine.

Galtee Foods

The Galtee Pig meat plant was originally planned to be built at the Kingston Castle site but was superseded by the milk Powder and Chocolate crumb so when the time came it was build in the late 60's on site on Cahir Hill and started production in 1968 with the inimitable Edwin Cussen at the helm. He certainly put Galtee meats on the global map and the plant went from success to success until his departure in 1979, there were many stories and photographs from all over the world but the best story I herd was one time he was returning from Heathrow when he met some Mitchelstown 'friends' while they were having a drink in the lounge in Heathrow one of the friends took his brief case and spread 20 or 30 condoms on the top of his documents. Now these were illegal in Ireland at the time so when at the customs in Cork he was asked to open his briefcase he was unfazed when the custom officer said ' these are illegal'   'Sorry 'said Edwin and taking a pin from his lapel took up each one and pierced it with the pin. When he had finished he turned to the officer and said 'OK you can have them now' and walked off' -- I don't know if its true, but it's a good story!!

A couple of other stories – yes stories!

The hole in the middle

One night in an adjacent town a group of lads were having a drinking session. They were acquaintances rather than friends and knew one another from GAA matches. At sometime late/ or early one of the four said ' I bet ye'd love a bit of mate'. 'Jas I'd ate a scabby child' said another and yer man said 'hang on, I'm going out to the car' one of the others followed and when the boot was opened it was full of hams, rashers, sausages and puddings – so the two brought in a half ham and had a great ould feast and more drink. They finally went home well scuttered.

However the one who went out to the car with yer man was a Garda on leave and rang Galtee foods the following day. There was a big investigation and stocktake after stocktake revealed no discrepancy. All the van drivers were questioned and their vans also checked. A full stocktake was redone but no discrepancy was found. After hours and hours of discussion one young checker asked if he could try a theory he had, this was approved and he went off to the main chill store and got the fork lift driver to move the pallets on an outside section to find that there was no product in the centre, which was assumed to be full of product. The 'hole in the middle' represented tens of tons of meat products some of which ended up in the boot of the car.

There were prosecutions and convictions and fines - but the real culprits were never caught - but were known!!

The Resurrection Pigs

The other story was called 'the resurrection pigs' and goes like this. One Sunday afternoon Paddy O'Keeffe was watching a GAA match on TV and enjoying being by himself as the wife and kids had gone to their granny's for a visit. The match was good but Paddy was comfortably dozing when the phone rang.

O'Keeffe here' Said Paddy O'Keeffe

; Hello! Is that Paddy O'Keeffe the pig agent for the factory?'

Suddenly startled Paddy grabbed the phone, nearly letting it fall ' Hello! Paddy 'yes! That's me, who am I speaking to?'

'This is the Garda Sergeant in town, any chance you could come in - there's something I want to talk to you about but not on the phone'

'When do you want me, I'm not too busy to morrow' Paddy told the Sergeant

'Well its kind of urgent, any chance you could call in now?'

Paddy was a little startled 'Sure! I can I'll see you in 15 or 20 minutes'. 'Thanks! Mr O'Keeffe, I'll see you then'

Twenty minutes later Paddy pulled up the Cortina outside the Garda barracks in Upper Cork Street and entered the barracks at the top of Upper Cork Street. Going into the public office Paddy announced himself to the duty Garda. 'I'll get the Sergeant' he replied and disappeared in a side door'. In a moment the tall broad sergeant appeared smiling and offering his hand 'Mr O'Keeffe many thanks for coming' he greeted 'pass through the door here and come into my office' Paddy entered a small, well appointed tidy office and sat down on the chair in front of the desk. The Sergeant looked him in the eye and introduced 'I'm Tom O'Connor, please call me Tom, again I'm grateful to you for coming at such short notice' Paddy replied 'Nice to meet you I'm Paddy as you know', what's all this about?!!

Well' replied Tom 'its like a shaggin fairytale. Do you know that you're buying you're own pigs back a second time'.

'Jasus! You're having me on Tom, what do you mean?'

Well,' replied the Sergeant 'I was sceptical myself but the Super in Fermoy had heard a rumor and when a labouring position was known to be going in the pig factory area he got one of his detective garda's to apply for it, its like a Mike Hammer novel !. Anyway this young detective – we'll call him Jer- has been working in the factory cleaning out the pens and the yard for the last two weeksand is now sure that there's a scam on between Dan the bear- the supervisor in the pen area – and Mickie Joe Reilly the pig haulier and it goes like this'

Paddy O'Keeffe looked stunned at the Sergeant and nodded to go on. 'Well' continued the Sergeant ' Mickie Joe is the haulier that gets rid of the sick pigs and disposes of them – he got this job from Dan the bear. So Mickie Joe brings in a load of pigs from Paddy the farmer and unloads them into the holding pens where a young checker would count them and weigh them and enter them into the received book. Mickie Joe heads off for his next load of pigs.

Some time later Jer was cleaning out some hundred yards away and saw Dan in the pen with the new load of pigs and then disappearing into the factory building. About 5.30 an inspection of all the pigs in the pens was made to see if they that they were all fit for the night killing shift. Of the 500 or so in the pens eight were lying out cold and were removed to the reject pen for collection by the reject haulier – who happened to be Mickie Joe and so when he arrived about 6.30 a.m he loaded the sick pigs and went off to dispose of them –however Jer had marked all eight during the night while no one was around. Mickie Joe went home and put all the eight in a shed. The following morning some four or five would be right as rain having got over the sedative that Dan had injected on his visit to the pen and so after about 10 days Mickie Joe had a full load of 'his own' pigs for the factory.

This scam had been going on for nearly a year but we will be doing a full search on Wednesday the day we expect the delivery and we would like you to be present. Paddy was nearly speechless and blurted out 'it's like a detective story – of course I'll be there – will I have a word with the manager?' 'No' replied the Sergeant'. We don't want anyone else involved until the search is finished'.

So Paddy went home still stunned and on the Wednesday went to the factory and met Jer and another plain clothes Sergeant from Fermoy. They found Dan the Bear in the pen area and asked him about the sick pigs. The DS from Fermoy had a warrant to search Dan's locker where they found syringes and enough sedative to knock out an elephant. Faced with this, Dan sang the song blaming Mickie Joe for getting him into the scam. Mickie Joe, unsuspecting, arrived with 'his own' load of pigs. When they were examined, the mark put on by Jer was clear on five, Mickie Joe was lead away. Management were called and were shocked.

The two bucks were duly charged and six months later in the circuit court they each got twelve months and £1,000 fine. A whole new set of buying rules were put in place including tagging of all purchased pigs but Dan the Bear and Mickie Joe will not be forgotten as the instigators of the resurrection pigs.

Sadly it's now it's gone. All meat imported and the site flattened – progress?!

E.M. Edwin Cussen founder of Galtee Foods, holding Galtee 'Tender Made' Bacon on the Wall of China - a symbol of Galtee's dreams of expansion into the Asian market, of which Cussen was a great advocate.

(Bill Power Collection)

Killeshandra Creamery, County Cavan, in 1911. Now known as Lakelands Co-op, by 2010, it had become one of the oldest surving co-operative societies in Ireland, as by then, most other societies had merged with other societies.

Dicksgrove Creamery was taken in 1917 by one of two German prisoners of war who were on the run from the British army. They succeeded in escaping and made their way back to Germany from where one of them sent this photograph to the then creamery manager, Thomas Dennehy.

7

Hazelbrook Dairy - Hughes Brothers

In 1961 I joined Hughes Brothers Dairy in Rathfarnham. At the time this was the largest of the dairies in the Dublin District Milk Board area and the largest bottler of liquid milk for urban consumption in the whole island of Ireland. It supplied more than 40,000gallons of milk daily to its customers. My job was dairy Chemist in the laboratory, responsible for the physical, chemical and micro-biological quality of the milk sold.

The Hughes Brothers James, George and William started the Hughes Bros. bottle milk dairy in Rathfarnham, Co Dublin in 1926. They took over their father's herd at Hazelbrook Farm and started making house to house deliveries by horse and cart around south County Dublin, such as the nearby villages of Rathfarnham and Dundrum.

Hazelbrook House original farm home of the Hughes family, situated inside the gate of the Dairy in Rathfarnham. It was where the Author did his interview with Billy Hughes. Now rebuilt at Bunratty Folk Village Co Clare.

155

Their milk being of high quality the further improved it by being the first to pasteurise bottled milk, which made it safer for the fight against TB and to combat the high infant mortality in Dublin at that time and was distributed by horse drawn drays and went from strength to strength. In order to use surplus milk they started to make ice cream. During the 1920's the average wage inn Dublin was about £2.50 per week, it became a tradition to splash out on a pint brick of HB ice cream for the Sunday lunch.

When I joined HB in 1961 it was a big operation in both milk and ice cream having 80% + of the Irish Ice Cream Market and the largest bottled milk supplier in the Dublin Region. HB had been refinanced in 1939 and was a private company controlled by a Board of directors which was a list of some of the Dublin elite. William (Bill) Freeman was Managing Director and William (Billy) Hughes assistant Managing Director and with Mr Pat Grey as General Manager.

Billy Hughes was the only son of James Hughes the driving force of the three brothers and was the only member of the founding family working in the business. Both worked fulltime at Hazelbrook. Billy Hughes would arrive at 8.45 each morning in his Mark II Jaguar 3.4 and was a real gentleman and a caring employee. Bill Freeman arriving at 9.0a.m in a variety of cars changing every few months, I can recall a white two door Ford Classic Coupe for some months, however every Saturday morning he would glide in about 10.00 a.m. in the Rolls-Royce Silver Cloud, for a wash, a valet and a polish in the garage. Both had offices in the original Hazelbrook farmhouse which now stands reconstructed in the Bunratty Folk Park Co. Clare. (See above)

Liquid milk for human consumption was very different in its requirements to that for butter or cheese which was (and is) known as manufacturing milk. The farmers supplying liquid milk were required to sign a contract with the District Milk Board and with the dairy. The biggest difference was the requirement to supply milk throughout the 12 month period. This required the farmer to have half his herd calving in winter and the other half in summer so that there was a constant milk supply throughout the year. For this they received a premium price for milk which was paid per gallon of milk instead of per lb of butterfat as in the creameries.

The farmers supplying milk to Hughes Bros. came from Counties Dublin, Meath, Kildare and Wicklow numbering some 3000. These were collected on a daily basis, from a stand on the main road near the farm gate and the washed empties left, by a fleet of trucks. The cans were standardised to 10 gal aluminium and were stacked 2 high on the trucks.

The trucks would start to arrive at the intake from the farms about 8.30am and the cans would be placed on the conveyer which carried them to the tipper at the scales. The lid was removed and placed on the lid wash conveyer; the empty can went to the can washer, coming out the far side joined with its lid and back on the truck.

Winter collection was another story particularly in Wicklow when the snow came. We had a very bad winter in, I think, 1962 and the trucks went out for the milk but 2 did not get back for 4 days. One of the oldest drivers – we'll call him

Rare photo of collection truck in Wicklow.

Mick – was with HB since it started and knew the 'big boss' well and so when he got stranded in a snow drift he makes way to the nearest phone and calls the Managing Director Bill Freeman directly who told Mick to get to the nearest pub and have a few whiskeys on the company, Of course Mick knew that this would happen and that was why he did not call the garage.

Another incident was the other driver who found himself with a drift across the road some 10 -15 feet long and seemingly soft snow. Himself and a couple of farmers were planning to back up and drive the truck fast through the drift when they saw a man struggling through the snow in the field and frantically waving his arms and shouting 'stop, stop, my car is buried in that drift' so they dug in and found it. If he had been 15 mins late his car would have been smashed as the truck drove its way through.

Milk and water
The farms were well selected by the milk contracts manager John Somers and were equipped with modern facilities and milk coolers thus the milk was rarely sour if ever. The main quality problem that had to be contended with was water in the milk since on fortnightly butterfat test was done like in the creameries. The problem was not a very large one and it was nearly always the same group who were sure they could get away with it.

The test method used in the 50's for the absolute detection of water in milk was the freezing point method. A tedious and complex test, so when it was set up it was usual to do up to 8 or even 10. However since the milk was frozen by means of supercooled ether it had its difficulties. The ether was cooled by passing a current of air through the ether so that by the end of 8 tests the ether had spread throughout the lab and us operatives were nearly asleep, even with extraction fans which were nowhere as efficient as in these days. In any case we always managed to prove the presence of water in our real suspects and they would be good – at least for some months.

One of my jobs relating to this difficulty was the farm visit, particularly if a new supplier farm was found with adulterated milk (water added). In most cases it would be a mistake such as not fully draining the rinse water, but since the provision of can washing by the dairy was introduced, this could not be used as an excuse.

Most visits were routine but an odd one would remain in your memory. This particular incident happened in Co Meath not more than 20 miles from Dublin. It was a water-in- milk situation and the farm was in its first year supplying. The test over three days in one weer showed between 12 and 18 % water in the milk which was very serious. The farm was situated in an isolated area of Co Meath, this was 1962 and there were no other farms for miles. A young man of about 20 came out and invited me in. On entering the farm kitchen-living room the mother was sitting at the kitchen table. A strange looking woman in her late 50's with long unkempt strealish hair. She poured out tea into a well used mug and slopped some milk into it while saying, 'Welcome Sir, Mickie will show we the cow shed in a minute, drink up the tae now'.

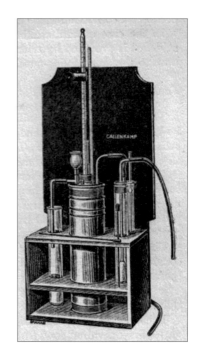

Test for added water.

The kitchen table was unbelievable with four to six inches of mouldy breadcrumbs covering more than half the table it was very difficult to feel normal and even more difficult to drink the tea from a mug of indeterminable uses and washing. It was an unnerving place so I made my way to inspect the cow shed and the mlk cooling and storage area accompanied by 'Mickie' this boy/man who kept referring to a large open well in the yard, in which his young sister and two dogs were drowned. I never got to see the equipment but made a beeline for my car outside the gate. There was a sigh of relief when I was driving away. Maybe it was all anxiety or nerves, but I'm not that way affected. Subsequently we wrote to the farm a very serious letter and luckily this seemed to work as no more water was added to the milk. We did not sign a contract the following year.

Milk & Jets

There were many interesting farms supplying milk in those years. One which held a lot of interest to me was in North Dublin who had a pedigree Jersey herd and was a very wealthy family originally from England. On a routine visit I was looking at a framed photograph in the study which showed a gentleman with Sir Frank Whittle, inventor of the Jet engine whom I recognised. Asking the farm owner and explaining my interest in aviation he told me that the gentleman in the photograph was his father. He went on to tell the story that as a young man manufacturing burner assemblies for oil fired boilers, when he was approached by a local acquaintance – Frank Whittle to design burners for his developing jet engine. This he did and the rest is history. The burner became an integral part of the Whittle Jet Engine and Patent and so the family gets a royalty – just a few cents - from every burner in every jet engine manufactured in the world for ever and ever. No wonder he had a couple of hundred acres in North Dublin and a prize herd of some 100 Jersey cows!!!

Milk products division

This company division was the mainstay of the Dairy, pasteurising and bottling some 40,000 gallons of milk every day, seven days per week. This was a complex operation. The milk from the farmers being received from the collection trucks and first being pumped to the bank of raw milk tanks, each holding up to 6000 gallons and maintained at 38-40°F(2-3°C) until ready for Pasteurisation. This was of the latest technology complete with flow diversion valves in the event of the temperature dropping below the correct temperature milk was then cooled and held in the Pasteurised milk tanks awaiting bottling.

There were high speed bottle filling and capping units which filled at 1,500 gals. per hour which connected to sophisticated high speed bottle conveyors and automatic crate filling equipment – a long way from the initial operation in 1926. In those days the bottles were returned, inspected, washed and refilled. Some 30 to 40 runs were got from bottles. \The washers were also automatic and connected at the output end with a bottle conveyor which took the bottles direct to the filling line.

The pre-wash visual inspection was very important as one would not believe what people put into milk bottles. Some examples – Dead and live mice, young rats, frogs, small birds, snails, dog poo,

High speed bottle filling.

159

baby poo, pee, paint, petrol, paraffin oil, detergent, pesticides, poisons, diesel oil, many unmentionables and the list goes on. Most of these the bottle washers will cope with but some were impossible and the bottle had to be broken. Unfortunately an odd one gets through ending up in a complaint which came back through the milkman to end up on my door at the Quality Control Laboratory.

Complaints

Dealing with milk complaints in Dublin in the 1960's was a delicate process particularly in some of the inner city slums, Corpo. Estates and Corpo. Apartments, strangely often the most difficult were from the 'better' estates and the 'big' houses many of whom could be 'right bitches' and not letting out an odd 'desperate housewife'. The golden rule was; get the bottle back' and in most cases this simply required a couple of lbs of butter or a few blocks of ice cream. Often the most difficult were solved with the help of Eddie Robbins who was a master of plaamaas and diplomacy. |some did end up in court but were usually settled 'on the steps'. One added advantage of finding the addresses was that I knew Dublin better than many Dublin born.

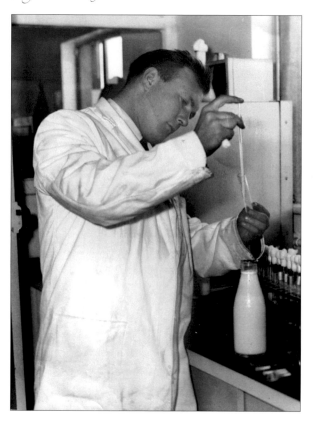

The author in the Milk control laboratory at Hughes Brothers Dairy, Hazelbrook, Rathfarnham.

Automatic crating.

Milk storage and delivery

When the milk crates came off the fillers they were stacked six high and wheeled into the clill store on specially designed hand carts awaiting for delivery the following morning. The engineer Paddy Moran introduce an innovation about this tine called the refrigerated garage where some 10-20 wholesale delivery trucks were readied for the morning with milk and other products and then parked in the the specially insulated and refrigerated garage so that many hours could be saved in loading in the morning – HB was very progressive in trying new ideas.

The retail sales were done by electric milk cart and by horse drawn dray of which some 10-15 were still operating in the 1960's. these four wheel drays in their distinctive dark blue with red piping were well known in South Dublin The Horses were grazed and stabled in the adjoining field at Nutgrove Avenue and looked after like babies. Bill Freeman the MD took a special interest in the horses and the transport ensuring the all vehicles were looking their best at all times. The painting of the drays and trucks was done on site and it was fascinating to watch the painter do the red stripes on the edges of the drays and some of the trucks,- truly a craftsman of high skill. Everything that promoted the HB image in both milk and ice cream was to a high standard way ahead of what many of the co-ops were doing at the same time.

Stacking milk crates in cold room.

HB Electric Milk Float in the 1960s.

Rare photograph of horse drawn Milk float.

HB ice cream

Further down the yard behind the dairy was the ice cream division ably managed by Ted Murphy This had three distinct sections one making ice cream mix and mix for ice lollies, the ice cream section filling pint bricks and tubs and then there was the frozen confections on a stick – the penny lolly an absolute favourite and so popular that one huge Gram machine was producing only the penny lolly in a variety of flavours up to 16 hours daily. Two other Gram machines were scheduled to produce the other stick confections like Choc ice, Brunch and al the other favourites. These machines were very versatile and could produce a wide range of shapes and coatings.

In 1966 a new million gallon factory was completed incorporating the newest in low temperature technology. The entire cold store was built on special insulation 'glass blocks'- a first outside USA and the fast freezing of products in the roof space on a 'Rollerbed' system, another first

The summer season was the peak of production and some 50 or more part time workers were hired for the packing and helping in the Ice cream when a second shift was utilised from 4 to 12 p.m. they were all worked hard as the machines kept producing and the product had to be packed but the banter and craic and the ska was to be heard to be believed and the stories were legion. One mar-

The pint brick – still selling in 2010.

120 cup filling – for the cinema!

ried eegit from the milk got involved with a 'young wan' and was going around asking could he get the wife to take in and mind the baby if the 'wan' got pregnant!! Anyway the wife heard the story and beat the hell out of him with a stick including a nice pair of shiners- he went back in his box!!!

At this time HB held more than 80% of the ice cream and frozen confectionery market in Ireland and the current facilities were getting too small year on year so a decision in principle to build a new factory on site was finalised this was late 1963. a lot of work was done into the planning of the new facility and the author was very involved and did Post-Graduate studies at Penn State University in 1964 including a thesis on a new Ice

HB icecream sales banner from the 1960s.

cream factory. During my time in the US the huge American conglomerate W.R.Grace acquired the company and the state of the art factory was started in 1965 when I returned- much of my thesis design was incorporated. The new factory started production in 1966/67 and new ice cream stores were built around the country to increase sales in the regions and the operation went from strength to strength. W.R. Grace sold the Ice Cream to Unilever and in a progression to nothing closed the HB Ice Cream plant in 2002 with a loss of 180 jobs.

A sad day, in a new verse to the 'Rare ould times' I pen

Now HB and the Lolly are gone. The factory long since closed down
Now the ice cream comes from Cavan
No more from Hazelbrook farm.

New Ice Cream delivery truck built in the HB coach building Department in 1964.

HB coach building department - showing Joe Quinlivan,
Paddy Timmons, Sean Farley and Jimmy Garavan.

W.W. Hughes (foreground left with glasses) with visitors and Ice Cream cakes – a favourite for Birthdays in the Dublin area.

HB chairman, W.L Freeman, (wearing hat) and visitors.

Department of Agriculture & Technical Instruction for Ireland.

Creamery Manager's Certificate.

Awarded

to   Peter Curtin

on the results of an examination in Theoretical subjects relating to creamery management, and in consideration of his having managed a Creamery to the satisfaction of the Department.

J.R. Meyrick

Secretary

30ᵗʰ November   1925.

A rare example of the Creamery Manager's Certificate, issued by the first Department of Agriculture and Technical Instruction for Ireland (DATI), issued in 1925.

8

Folklore, Druids and Kitty the Hare

Roots of dairy folklore, Brehon Laws & dairying superstitions

The Romans never invaded Ireland, but it is widely accepted that they were well aware of the country and its people. The Roman geographer, Pomponius Mela, recorded that Irish cattle 'burst' if they were allowed to feed too long. The Roman historian, Gaius Julius Solinus, wrote that

Ireland has such excellent pastures that cattle are brought to the danger of their lives by overfeeding except now and then they are driven out of their fields. As in many other countries cattle in Ireland were herded to protect them from wolves and raiders and to keep them from straying Herding was for many , away of life The Buachaill or aodhaire were herdsmen and the position held a certain status in the community.

It is clear that the herdsman looked on himself as superior to the ploughman, and the cattle breeder, the owner of large herds, was apt to look down on the husbandman whose back was bent over the spade.

It also implied a great deal more than simply keeping the animals from straying. The young boys who usually served as herdsmen were expected to keep the calves from sucking the cow's milk once they were old enough to eat grass, so as to keep the milk for human consumption or for making butter.

Stories of the herding boyhood of many Irish saints feature a similar picture :
'The boy traces a line on the ground between the calves and the cows with the point of his bachall or staff and neither the cows nor the calves will cross it – a sort of prototype electric fence'.

Thr safe-keeping the cattle were driven home at nightfall, and sometimes shared the family dwelling. This was regarded as appropriate, because milch cattle were closely associated with the woman of the house, who was often in charge of milking. It afforded greater protection , too. As the Annals of Innisfallen, (1028AD) noted 'Great snow... in Lent... for three days and nights... so that neither people nor cattle left their houses'.

Some cattle were shut up in a lios or roofless enclosure surrounded by a wattle fence with the calves occupying a separate area. Another type of enclosure was called a tour, and the name has survived to the present day in place names like Tooreenagrena.

In summer, cattle herds were often driven off for several months to hill and

Mountain pastures, usually accompanied by women who herded them and also milked them and who lived in 'booley' huts on the pastures. Buailteachas or Booleying survived in Ireland to the last century and many Booley huts are still evident in the West Cork and Kerry hills and mountains.

A good account of booleying in the Galtee mountains, County Tipperary, was recorded in 1940. This account refers to the period around 1875.

> *Comaointeas is what we used to call this going up on the mountain with the cattle in the old times. The entire mountain was held as commonage by a number of people who lived at the foot of the mountain, and they used to send the cattle up in spring and bring them down again in the autumn. About the middle of April was the time they started to go up to the buaile as we used to call the house and they would bring them down again at the beginning of November. The reason for going up at all was that there was no rent on the mountain and the land on the farm below was nearly all put to hay to feed the cows in the wintertime. In that way a farmer could have a lot more cattle on a small farm. There used to be a house at the buaile, and some of the family used to spend the whole summer above with the cattle. Sometimes it was the young ones that went up, and sometimes it was the old people, if there was a lot of work to be done below, and they wanted the young people there to do it. They would live in the houses on the mountain all the summer and only come down to Mass and when they were bringing down the butter. About from twenty to forty cattle each one would have on the mountain. The houses were by themselves with a mile or more between them, so it was kind of lonely sometimes up there, but other times they would come together and have a dance or some other fun like that.*

The work they did was to milk the cattle morning and evening and make butter. When enough was made they brought it down to the road to be carried to the town (Mitchelstown). They would bring it down the mountain in a firkin that the cooper used to make, for in those days the cooper was an important tradesman in the district and he got plenty to do.

In May they used to plant potatoes up on the mountain near the buaile. 'Black potatoes' we used to call them, and I used to hear the old people saying that the light never came in them until the Famine year. They used to cut the green stalks and feed them to the cattle, and it would be nearly November when they dug the last of the potatoes on the mountain. Potatoes and buttermilk they used to eat mostly, and they had fresh milk and the butter and oaten meal bread, and, I hear and odd drop of poitin

> *What stopped the comaointas in this district was this: as long as the mountain was rent –free it paid the farmers to sent up the cattle, but about sixty five years ago or maybe a bit more the landlord of the place, old Kingston of Mitchelstown, put a rent of three pounds a head on every cow that was on his tenants' land, and of course that took away whatever profit the farmers had out of the comaointeas . The cows were taken away from any one that did not pay the new rent and put in the pound, and sold of if they were not paid for. That*

*was not so easy to do, because the farmers would not bring in the cattle and the
'wattlemen' had to go out on the mountain themselves and catch the cattle. But
in a short time all the cattle were seized, or sold by the farmers because they
could not pay the new rent, and from that time on they kept only as many cattle as they could feed on their own farms.*

In Ireland milking was done by both sexes, but a reading of information surviving
from ancient and mediaeval days indicates that it was regarded as being the special
province of women. The patron of the dairy was St. Brigid of Kildare who had
spent the greater part of her youth working in the family dairy. Legend holds that
no matter how much of the dairy's produce she bestowed on the poor, she was
always miraculously enabled to produce yet another churnful. It appears that St.
Brigid took over from a pagan goddess of the same name. A number of writers have
averted to this:

> *It is in the person of her Christian namesake St.Brighid that the pagan goddess
> survives best. For if the historical element in the legend of St. Brighid is slight,
> the mythological element is correspondingly extensive, and it is clear beyond
> question that the saint has usurped the role of the goddess and much of her
> mythological tradition The saints life infers a close connection with livestock
> and the produce of the earth.*

Dairying and cattle in ancient Ireland was far more central to daily life than it is in
modern times. Cattle, milk and Milk products as a result, became currency for
financial dealings, outward symbols of community status, material for epic poetry
and the spoils of war.

For example, the central story of the Ulster Cycle of traditional Irish tales is
Tain Bó Cuailnge ,The Cattle Raid Of Cuailnge. This is and epic narrative which
tells of an expedition by the combined forces of four provinces, led by Maeve of
Connacht, to carry off by force a great bull possessed by one of the landowners of
Ulster.

Generally, because of their vital place in rural living, cattle'appear to have been
the main standard of value, and in any considerable transactions the medium of
exchange as well'

This system was recognised by the Brehon Laws, one of the earliest codified
legal systems, which dealt comprehensively with cows, their value, ownership and
legal significance. Under these laws, a divorced woman was entitled to one sixth of
the produce of the churn after her husband left her. And, because dairy produce
had for connotations of status, one law tract even laid down the proper food for fos-
ter children of different castes:

> *The children of the inferior grades are fed to bare sufficiency on stirabout made
> of oatmeal on buttermilk or water, and it is taken with stale butter. The sons of
> the chieftain grades are fed to satiety on stirabout made from barley meal upon
> new milk, taken with fresh butter. The sons of kings are fed on stirabout made
> from wheaten meal upon new milk taken with honey.*

Cattle raiding

In less peaceful times milk cattle were both the tribute of the vanquished and the focus for warlike forays. The ancient annals record many instances of cattle raiding carried out by kings, princes and other important men. In fact one modern historian suggests that cattle-raiding had all the appearances of and organised sport' and suggests that 'the cattle raid was the ancient equivalent of the detective story of today'.

There is of course a very close parallel with the cattle rustling in the US Wild West in the 19th century but the Irish raids really put these in the halfpenny place as to numbers. Figures for the numbers of cattle removed in such sallies are still extant.

> In 1044 the king of Aileach took 1,200 cows in Louth; in 1053 Mac Lochlainn took 300 cows in Derry-Tyrone, in 1056 Eochaidh Ua Flaithen took 500 cows in Antrim-Down; in 1062 Ardgar MacLochlainn took 1,000-3,000 cows in north east Ulster and in 1130, Conchobar Ua Lochlainn took 'many thousands' of cows in the same district.

A special class of literature celebrated these deeds and elevated their status to the heroic. Later records especially the English State Papers dealing with Ireland, document the survival od cattle raiding as an aspect and method of internal warfare. In 1562, Sussex, writing to the Queen, stated that Shane O'Neill had been in O'Donnell country and had 'taken 10,000 head of cattle'. In 1573 it was reported that Turlough Lynagh O'Neill had 'preyed the Baron of Dungannon of 30,000 kine'. In 1584 Lord Deputy Perrot reported that an attack on Sorley Boy MacDonnell owner of 50,000 cows had left him with 1500.

Not only did the successful cattle raid lower the status of the owner whose cows were taken, but it tended to induce his submission. Milk and milk products in ancient and mediaeval times were staple foods; the cornerstone of the people's diet, and removal of the source was a weapon of crucial importance.

In 1600 when the Lord Deputy marched to the North to establish a garrison at Lough Foyle, it was said that his advance gravely damaged the power of O'Neill because it forced his cattle, 'from plains into the woods and so for want of grass did starve their cattle and for want of milk, which was their food, distress the people'.

The making of butter goes back thousands of years. In Ireland the booley houses provided one location for Buttermaking. In time however the kitchen became the traditional place for housing the churn, with some farms having a dedicated room as a dairy. Butter is likely to have been originally made by agitating the cream in an animal skin container; in fact this is likely as the origin of cheese is reputed to have come from the storing of milk in the cured stomach of a calf where it curdled due to the pepsin enzyme residues. Small churns which have been excavated from bogs were hollowed out of a single solid piece of wood. Others were assembled from staves, such as the traditional type of Irish churn, the dash churn.

Kitty the Hare

I used to stay at my uncle Ned's (My father's brother) farm for a few days every summer, often it was late summer when the 'Pattern day' was held, centering on the holy well near the church.

One evening Ned referred to some old local woman as 'into piseogs' on asking him what were 'piseogs,' he avoided the question and said I was too young to know anything about that sort of stuff.

Relenting a day or so later he told me that in some families the women were said to have certain 'magic' powers particularly around May Eve, probably a throwback to the old pagan Ireland and the Gaelic Brehonic festival of Bealtaine. These women could put a curse on a farm when the cow could loose her calf or the potatoes would rot in the ground or they could steal the fat from the milk. He continued, saying that some of these women had the power of shape-changing and could turn their body into that of a hare so as to suck the milk out of the neighbour's cows.

That night he told me a story that he had been told many years before – when butter was made on the farms. One May Eve a farmer was keeping an eye on his farm and exercising his greyhounds at the same time, when rounding a hedge he spotted a hare suckling his cows. The hounds took off after the hare, but didn't she travel around in a big circle and jumped on to the farmers' shoulders to escape from

Rural Irish Kitchen circa 1890. *(George Morrison)*.

the hounds, before he could do anything the hare jumped from his back into a big furze bush and got away.

When in the same end of the farm the following year he called to a small cottage for a drink. The old lady in the house knew him by name and gave him a wholesome drink of buttermilk. When he asked how she knew his name she asked 'Do you not remember last May Eve when the hare jumped on your shoulder? I was that hare escaping from the hounds'

These hares could be shot, so it was thought, but only with a 'silver bullet' which was a pellet made from a florin (silver coin) which had a cross device on one face. There is a similarity here with the killing of 'vampires' (who suck blood) It apparently common for farmers to watch their farms and animals on May Eve and some were more vehement regarding this.

> Some people will not allow any person to walk their land for any purpose on May Day. A man about four miles from my own place in West Cork makes no secret of it that he would shoot any person, man or woman he'd catch walking through his land on May morning. He says 'what would bring them there, don't they know its May Day and don't they know what is said about such things on May Day? If they have no bad intention then they won't be found doing it, and if they come with a bad intention don't they deserve to be shot? And the man that would shoot such a person would be doing a good act for the neighbours.

Dairying superstitions

The dependency of Irish agriculture on cattle and dairying inevitably lead to much superstition growing up around the production of milk and butter and particularly since these activities were never totally predictable in their results and little if any of the science entailed was understood or even known.

> In the whole business of handling milk, luck was more important than labour, and Buttermaking in particular was a task fraught with unseen dangers. Often the butter would mysteriously refuse to break, and many were the precautions taken and remedies sought. It seems that the old Irish method was to churn from whole milk and it was customary until recently to pour the skim milk into the churn along with the risen cream. It should be remembered to that the butterfat content was low, and since many peasant farmers had not more than one cow at a time in milk, its quality would be more variable than the milk of a large herd. The unaccountable variations in the success of churning were widely attributed to the intervention of fairies of witches.

The oldest recorded buttermaking incantation is a diplomatic mixture of pagan and Christian prayer. Later purely Christian prayers were developed for the purpose of helping the churning along. In the life of Saint Colman, a seventh century monk, it was recorded that after the churning 'He blessed the buttermilk and there came out of it a great curd'.

Traditionally many precautions were taken for the protection of the cows and the dairy. 'The cow house or byre was built on a site which would not prevent the passage of fairies or encroach on their territory(mainly the fairy fort) crosses made of straw and other materials on St. Brigid's Eve were hung in the cowhouse or fixed to the doors and windows. It was hoped to protect the cows themselves by tying red ribbons to their tails or around their necks; rings made of rowan were similarly applied for the same purpose. Cattle were driven across the dying flames of bonfires for the same purpose. Cattle were driven across the dying bonfires on May Eve and Saint John's Eve, or between two of these fires. So too were they forced to swim in a lake or river to avert illness or bad luck.

A goat was generally kept with herds of cows' to bring them luck'. I have heard this custom explained by saying that goats had the capacity for eating poisonous herbs without being fatally affected, which was not the case with cattle. Another animal which was regarded as lucky in a herd was a maighdean bhuaile (a cow which had never borne a calf). Holy water was of course often sprinkled on livestock and scores of charms (apocryphal folk-prayers) were recited to avert or cure the many diseases from which they might suffer, whether through natural causes or as the folk often suspected, through the evil eye of an unfriendly neighbour. The fairies too were blamed for causing animals to be 'elf-shot'. This was due to the fact that ailing cows with pierced hides might be found grazing near a place where small stone arrow- heads from ancient times were often found lying about: the fairies were immediately blamed for having cast these weapons at the cows in an attempt to take them off into fairyland. One of the remedies for 'elf-shot' was to give the stricken animal a drink of water in which the 'fairy arrows 'had been boiled.

As soon as a cow calved she was ceremoniously blessed with holy water and fire while the following prayer was recited three times

Go mbeannai Dia dhuit, a bho!
Go mbannaithear faoi dodho lough!
Go Mbeannai an triur ata I bhfaitheas De
Mar ata : An t-Athair agus an Mac agus an Spiorad Naomh!
Tar aNaomh Michael Ard-aingeal, agus beannaigh an mart
In ainm an Athar agus an Mhic agus an Spioraid Naofa,
Agus Amen, a Dhia

TRANSLATION
God's blessing on thee O cow!
Twice blest be thee o calf!
\May the three who are in Heaven bless you:
The Father and the Son and the Holy Spirit!
Come saint Michael the Archangel and bless the beef
In the name of the Father and the Son and of the Holy Spirit.
Amen, O God.)

Although it was commonly accepted that the fairies who lived in the forts might need milk and take it from the cows on the farm, this was not resented, as people wished to live in amity with their otherworld neighbours. Precautionary measures were directed more against evil minded neighbours, who were liable to endeavour to steal one's milk or butter 'profit' (sochar an bainne) by magic means. Newly-calved cows stood in need of special protection, as their supply of milk was assured. Crushed flowers, such as marsh marigold, were rubbed to their udders, which were also singed with the flame of a blessed candle. The first stream of milk drawn from such a cow was allowed to fall to the ground 'for those who might need it' (the fairies presumably), and then a cross was marked on the cow's flank with some of her milk.

Festival of Bealtaine

A charred sod of turf from the Midsummer bonfire was placed in the milk-house as protection. The greatest care was taken not to loose one's milk-luck through negligence, as witness the following taboos : don't give away any milk on New Year's Day, on May Day, on any Monday or on a Friday: don't lend a milk-vessel; don't take to fetch water from well s vessel which is milk stained; when such a vessel has been washed, do not throw the cleansing water into a river or stream; don't give milk to a neighbour unless salt has been put into it; don't allow milk out of the house, if anybody is ill there.

It was a traditional custom never to drink milk on Good Friday; even the baby in the cradle, it is said, had to cry three times on that day before milk was fed to it. Another old-time custom, when goats were very numerous was to drink their milk in the belief that it cured tuberculosis. Ballykinlar in County Down and Goatstown in Co. Dublin were famous over a century ago in this regard, and thousands of patients came there, even from Scotland, to drink goat's milk.

Farmers were constantly afraid in days gone by that their milk and butter 'profit' could be stolen from them by evil-minded hags, who either bailed a neighbour's well or dragged a cloth over the dew of his fields on May Morn, saying 'come to me'! People sat up all night on May Eve to guard their wells and fields against such spells. It was believed in Ireland, as well as in many other countries, that such human hags had the power of changing themselves into hares and sucking the milk from the udders of cows. These hares could be shot, so it was believed, only with a 'silver bullet' (a pellet made from a florin which had a cross-device on one face).

Just as at calving-time, precautions had to be taken at churning –time against the evil intentions and the wiles of others. In the old days, there were no creameries in the rural areas and farmers churned their milk at home. The churn was deemed to be especially vulnerable to those who were thought to be disposed to steal the 'butter profit'. Every effort was therefore made to guard it against such enemies; a lice cinder was placed under the churn (many churns had charred bottoms in olden times from this practice) as well as an ass or hose shoe; in other districts nails of iron would be driven into the timber of a churn to protect it or else a withy of rowan-tree was bound around it. The tongs were kept in the fire during the period of churning, and water or fire-ashes were not allowed out of the house until the operation had ended. So too the fire was guarded: if anybody came to a house while churning was in progress and tried to take fire out of the house (by reddening his pipe or otherwise), he was prevented from doing so and forced to take a 'brash' (hand) at the churn before leaving in this way keeping the churn and its butter from harm.

Bog butter

For many years it was believed that the burial of butter in bogs had superstitious overtones, although it is now seen as an early attempt at conservation using the cool and sterile conditions of the bog.

The custom dates back as far as the sixth century at least and continued until the end of the eighteenth. The practice of preserving butter in bogs or moist earth is also found also in Scandinavia, Iceland, India, Morocco and Russia.

Throughout the nineteenth and early twentieth centuries as turf cutting reached down to the levels of the original burials many finds of bog butter were made. A local parish priest, having made such a find twelve feet deep, recorded that it still re-tained... .the marks of the hand of the ancient dame who pressed it into its present shape'.

Many beliefs grew up to explain the burial of butter in this way. One theory was that the butter was buried as a votive offering, perhaps as an inducement to the gods for the cure of a sick cow.

However, the most likely explanation is practical rather than magical. It is that bog land was used to preserve the butter by protecting it from daytime heat. The exclusion of air and the turf's sterile qualities would have prevented the growth of mould. In summer and autumn when butter was plentiful it made to store the surplus for the lean months of winter.

The added advantage was the extra flavour imparted by such storage. An account of Irish food of 1681 mentions 'Butter layed up in wicker baskets and mixed with... a sort of garlic and buried for some time in a bog to make provision of a high taste for Lent'

175

Knocklong Creamery, County Limerick. Buttermaking in the late 1930s or early 1940s.
Knocklong was taken over by Mitchelstown Co-op which closed it in the 1980s.
Below is the creamery as it stood in 2010.

9
Creameries 1955

List of Central and Auxiliary Creameries in Ireland

The following pages contain information on the central and auxiliary creameries in Ireland in 1955/'56. and are reproduced with the kind permission and co-operation of the then Irish Creamery Managers Association (Now the Dairy Executives Association). There are some unique aspects to this information particularly the nearest railway station and shows the huge social changes in rural Ireland since this time – a short period in most people's minds! It is fascinating to look at the Railway stations and the extent of the rail network in these days.

Rail was used extensively by the Co-ops for the transport of wholesale cream in twenty gallon churns especially for the Dublin market, including cream for the manufacture of ice cream by HB, Merville and Lucan in these years, and also to transport butter in one-pound wrapped rolls.

For those readers who had a relative who worked as a Creamery Manager in these years, it is likely that his name is in the lists.

The number of Central Creameries in 1956 was 174. It is now 27. There were 440 separating and Auxiliary Creameries virtually all of these are now gone or put to another use.

The main butter making creamery for the Condensed Milk CMompany of Ireland in Tipperary Town, in the 1950s.

List of Central and Auxiliary Creameries in Ireland
1956

Arranged distinctively under their respective Counties, with their nearest Railway Stations and Telegraphic Offices (or Telegraphic Addresses) Telephone Numbers and Names of Managers

ABBREVIATIONS-C.D.S.- Co-operative Dairy Society Ltd. These are registered under the Industrial and Provident Societies Acts and are owned by Farmers. In many cases such Societies supply their members with Seeds, manures, and other Agricultural requirements. The same remarks apply to C0-operative Agricultural and Dairy Societies **(C.A & D.S.)**. and Co-operative Creameries Ltd. **(C.C.Ltd)**. Most of these Societies have been organised by the Irish Agricultural Organisation Society (The Plunkett House, Dublin

N.D.C. – Newmarket Dairy Co. Head Office :- Mac Curtain Street, Cork

D.D. Co. Ltd. – Dairy Disposal Co. Ltd. – Head office : 5 South Frederick Street, Dublin

C.M. Co. – Condensed Milk Co. of Ireland (1928) Ltd (formerly known as Cleeves). Head Office: - Limerick.
(all the Creameries of this Company have been purchased by the Government).

NOTES - **" Auxiliary" Creameries.** – At auxiliary Creameries or separating stations, the cream is merely extracted from the milk and forwarded to a 'Central' Creamery for manufacturing into butter. Auxiliary Creameries belong to the owner or owners of the 'Central' to which they supply the cream. Independent auxiliaries are 'independent' each merely paying the 'Central' so much per cwt. for manufacturing and selling its butter.

In the Auxiliary creameries list, the name of the Central creamery receiving the cream supplies is shown in the brackets after the name of the creamery

' Central Creameries' – The word 'Central' is applied to all creameries which not only separate the cream from the milk , but also manufacture it into butter. In some cases each has also a number of 'Auxiliaries' supplying it with cream. Farmers' Central Creameries are all independent of one another.

[Under the Dairy Produce Act (1924), the term 'Creamery' is not applied to what has always been generally known as , and what is still popularly called 'An Auxiliary'. In the Act the words 'Cream Separating Station' are used instead of Auxiliary]

LIST OF CENTRAL CREAMERIES

Name of Creamery & Owners	DP Act 1924 Reg. No.	Post Town	Miles to Nearest Railway Station	Telephone No Telegraphic Address	Name of Manager
Co Cavan Annagelliffe C.D.S. Ltd	C.236	Oldcastle	Oldcastle 1/ 18	'Creamery , Oldcastle' Telephone ; Oldcastle 111	T.McLoughlin
Baileboro' C.A& D.S Ltd	C. 176	Baileboro'	Kingecourt 8	'Creamery, Baileboro' Telephone 3 Baileboro'	M.Fay J. O'Neill
Killeshandra C.A.& D.S. Ltd	C. 106	Killeshandra	Killeshandra	'Creamery, Killeshandra	B. Lavin
Kilnaleck C.A. & D.S. Ltd	C. 324	Kilnaleck	Oldcastle 8	Telephone No 3 'Creamery, Kilnaleck	

LIST OF CENTRAL CREAMERIES (cond.)

Name of Creamery & Owners	DP Act 1924 Reg. No.	Post Town	Miles to Nearest Railway Station	Telephone No Telegraphic Address	Name of Manager
Co Clare					
North Clare (D.D Co. Ltd)	C.360	Ennistymon	Ennistymon 0.5	'Creamery, Ennistymon 'Phone Ennistymon 6 & 26	D. O'Hanlon
East Clare (D.D.Co. Ltd)	C. 349	Scariff	Limerick 22	'Creamery, Scariff' Phone ; Scariff 8	Sean Sheehan
West Clare (D.D.Co.Ltd)	C. 359	Kilrush	Kilrush .25	'Creamery, Kilrush ' Phone Kilrush 7 & 22	M. Lane
Bunratty C.D.S. Ltd	C 362	Bunratty, Limerick	Sixmilebriddge 3.5	'Bunratty Creamery' Phone Bunratty 1	P.J. Cahill
Co CORK					
Allensbridge Co-op. Cry. Ltd	C. 160	Newmarket	Newmarket 2	Allensbridge Creamery, Newmarket, Cork' Phone Newmarket 31	C. O'Leary
Bandon C.A.& D.S. Ltd	C. 222	Watergate St, Bandon	Bandon	'Creamery Bandon' Phone Bandon 49	J. Treacy
Ballyclough C.A.& D.S. Ltd	C.327	Mallow	Mallow	'Creamery Mallow' Phone Mallow 2	P. J. Power
Barryroe C.C. Ltd	C. 168	Lislevane, Timoleague.	Timoleague 4	'Creamery Lislevane, Cork' Phone Lislevane 2	M. Collins
Boherbue C.A.& D.S .Ltd	C. 313	Boherbue	Banteer 9	'Creamery, Boherbue' Phone 4	A. O'Connor BSc
Castlelyons Co-op Cry Ltd	C. 130	Fermoy	Fermoy 5	'Creamery Castlelyons' Phone Castlelyons 2	T. O'Donnell P.C.
Castletownbere Creamery Co. (D.D. Co Ltd)	C. 366	Castletownbere	Bantry 33	'Creamery Castletownbere' Phone Castletownbere 3	D. O'Sullivan
Clondrohid Co-op Cry Ltd	C134	Clondrohid, Macroom.	Macroom 3.5	'Creamery Clondrohid, Macroom' Phone Clondrohid 2	J. J. Leahy
Coachford Creamery (N.D. Co)	C.113	Coachford	Cork 15	'Creamery Coachford' Phone Coachford 3	T. Gleeson
Drinagh Co-op Creamery Ltd	C.305	Drinagh	Drimoleague 6	'Co-operative Drinagh' Phone Drinagh 3, 6 & 7	W. J. Quirke

LIST OF CENTRAL CREAMERIES (cond.)

Name of Creamery & Owners	DP Act 1924 Reg. No	Post Town	Miles to Nearest Railway Station	Telephone No Telegraphic Address	Name of Manager
Dromtariffe C.C. Ltd	C.304	Banteer	Banteer 5	'Dromtariffe Cry, Kanturk' Phone Clonbanin Cross 3	J Buckley
Experimental Creamery, University College	C.356	Cork	Glanmire	Telephone Cork 21201	M. O'Shea, BA, MSc D.Ph Professor of Dairy Technology
Freemount Dairy Society Ltd	C.155	Charleville	Charleville 12	'Dairy Freemount' Phone Freemount 3	T.F. Crimmins
Kilcorney. C.D.S. Ltd	C.256	Rathcoole, Banteer.	Rathcoole 1.5	'Kilcorney Creamery Rathcoole' Phone Rathcoole (Co Cork) No.10	Jas. D. Hegarty
Killumney. C.D.S. Ltd	C.174	Ovens	Killumney	'Cry Killumney Ballincollig' Phone Ballincollig 2	P.J. Hurley
Lisavard C.A.& D.S. Ltd	C. 311	Clonakilty	Clonakilty 4	'Cry. Lisavard, Clonakilty, Phone Clonakilty 34	M.F. O'Donovan. BSc
Lombardstown C.A.& D.S. Ltd	C.151	Lombardstown	Lombardstown	'Creamery Lombardstown' Phone Lombardstown 2	D.J. Ryan
Milford Co-op Creamery Ltd	C.295	Milford, Charleville	Charleville 8	'Dairy Milford, Cork' Phone Milford 3	P. Noonan
Mitchelstown C.C Ltd.	C.238	Mitchelstown	Fermoy 9	'Creameries' Phone Mitchelstown 251/2	J.J .Lynch
Muskerry & Lissarda C.C. Ltd	C. 116	Farnanes	Cork 14	'Cloughduv Cry Crookstown' Phone Crookstown 7	P. McCarthy
North Cork Co-op Creameries Ltd.	C.287	Kanturk	Kanturk	'Creamery Kanturk' Phone Kanturk 3	C. O'Keeffe
Newmarket C.D.S. Ltd	C.154	Newmarket	Newmarket	'Creamery Newmarket Cork' Phone Newmarket 5	B. O'Connor
Shandrum Co-op Creamery Ltd	C.235	Newtownshandrum, Charleville	Charleville 5	'Creamery Newtown, Cork' Phone Newtown 3	M.J. Linehan

LIST OF CENTRAL CREAMERIES (cond.)

Name of Creamery & Owners	DP Act 1924 Reg. No	Post Town	Miles to Nearest Railway Station	Telephone No Telegraphic Address	Name of Manager
Terelton (Dairy D. Co Ltd)	C. 117	Terelton, Macroom	Cork 15	'Terelton Cry. Macroom' Phone Macroom 3	**E. O'Reilly**
West Cork Creameries (D.D. Co. Ltd)	C. 319	Aghadown, Skibbereen	Skibbereen 6	'Aghadown Creamery' Phone Churchcross 5	**P.J. Kerrisk**
Co Donegal					
Belleek C.D.S. Ltd	C.	Clyhore, Ballyshannon.	Belleek Ballyshannon 4	'Creamery, Clyhore, Ballyshannon.' Phone Clyhore 3	**J.V. Synnott**
Lagan C.D.S. Ltd	C. 209	Sallybrook, Manorcunningham	Sallybrook	'Cry Manorcunningham' Phone Manorcunningham 3	**W. Elder**
Co Kerry					
Abbeydorney C.D.S. Ltd	C. 159	Abbeydorney	Abbeydorney 1	'Creamery Abbeydorney' Phone Abbeydorney 3	**T.J. Brosnan BSc**
Ardfert (Dairy Disposal Co Ltd)	C.118	Ardfert	Ardfert 2	'Creamery Ardfert' Phone Ardfert 2	**John Blackwell**
Ballinclemessig C.D.S. Ltd	C.195	Ballyheigue, Tralee.	Ardfert 9	'Co-operate Ballyheigue'	**S. Fitzgerald**
Brosna C.A. & D.S. Ltd	C.133	Brosna	Abbeyfeale 8	'Brosna Cry. Abbeyfeale' Phone Brosna 4	**M. O'Connell**
Cahirciveen (D.D.Co Ltd)	C.365	Cahirciveen	Cahirciveen 3	'Creamery Cahirciveen' Phone Cahirciveen 7	**E. O'Mahony**
Castlemaine (D.D.Co.Ltd)	C.363	Castlemaine	Castlemaine	'Creamery Castlemaine' Phone Castlemaine 7	**J.A. Fitzgerald**
Dicksgrove (D.D. Co. Ltd)	C.219	Farranfore	Farranfore 3	'Dicksgrove Cry Farranfore' Phone Farranfore 3	**J. O' Regan BSc**

LIST OF CENTRAL CREAMERIES (cond.)

Name of Creamery & Owners	DP Act 1924 Reg. No	Post Town	Miles to Nearest Railway Station	Telephone No Telegraphic Address	Name of Manager
Dingle (D.D.Co.Ltd.)	C.361	Dingle	Dingle	'Creamery Dingl' Phone Dingle '3	**M. Droney**
Kenmare (D.D.Co.Ltd.)	C.364	Kenmare	Kenmare	'Creamery Kenmare' Phone Kenmare 5	**T. Coakley**
Lee Strand Co-op Creamery Ltd	C.301	Church St. Tralee	Tralee	'Unity Tralee' Phone Tralee 84	**Patk. O'Sullivan**
Listowel Creamery (D.D.Co. Ltd)	C.107	Listowel	Listowel	''Creamery Listowel' Phones Listowel 23, 80, 113	**T. O'Sullivan**
Lixnaw C.D.S. Ltd	C.316	Lixnaw	Lixnaw	'Creamery Lixnaw' Lixnaw 3	**J. H .Daly BSc**
Newtownsandes C.D.S. Ltd	C.153	Newtownsandes	Abbeyfeale 12	'Cry Newtownsandes' Phone Newtownsandes 3	**Michael Barrett**
Ratto Co-op (Agricultural & D.S. Ltd)	C.102	Ballyduff, Tralee	Lixnaw 5	'Invincible, Ballyduff, Kerry' Phone Ballyduff 3	**Wm. Sweeney**
Rathmore (D.D. Co. Ltd)	C.270	Rathmore	Rathmore	''Creamery Rathmore' Phone Rathmore 3	**B.O'Farrell**
Co Kilkenny					
Ballyhale (C.D.S.Ltd)	C. 277	Ballyhale	Ballyhale 1	''Creamery Knocktopher' Phone Knocktopher 3	**A.S. O'Loinsig**
Ballyragget (C.D.S. Ltd)	C. 343	Ballyragget	Ballyragget	'Creamery Ballyragget' Phone Ballyragget 7	**Michael O'Reilly**
Barrowvale C. Creamery Ltd	C. 114	Goresbridge	Goresbridge	'Creamery Goresbridge' Phone Goresbridge 5	**N. Fennelly**
Bennettsbridge Co-op Cry. Ltd	C. 252	Bennettsbridge	Bennettsbridge	'Creamery Bennettsbridge) Phone Bennettsbridge 4	**J. J. O'Brien**
Callan C.A.& D.S. Ltd	C. 123	Callen	Kilkenny 10	'Creamery Callen' Phone Callen 6	**P. Scriven**
Carrigeen C. D. S. Ltd	C. 210	Nr Waterford	Waterford 5	'Co-operative Waterford' Phone Mooncoin 3	**Gerald H. Kinlay**
Castlecomer, Co-op Cry Ltd	C. 140	Castlecomer	Castlecomer	'Creamery Castlecomer' Phone Castlecomer 209	**M. A. Teehan**

LIST OF CENTRAL CREAMERIES (cond.)

Name of Creamery & Owners	DP Act 1924 Reg. No	Post Town	Miles to Nearest Railway Station	Telephone No Telegraphic Address	Name of Manager
Castlehale C. D. S. Ltd	C. 142	Kilmoganny,,	Ballyhale 4.	'Creamery Kilmoganny' Phone Kilmoganny 3	R. Collins
Freshford C.D.S.Ltd	C. 216	Freshford	Ballyragget 6	'Creamery Freshford' Phone Freshford 10	T. Dwane
Glenmore Co-op Cry. Society Ltd.	C. 221	Glenmore, Waterford	Glenmore 1.5	'Creamery Glenmore' Phone Glenmore 2	T. P. Cuddihy
Ida C. C. Ltd	C. 163	Tullogher, New Ross	New Ross 4	'Ida Creamery New Ross' Phone New Ross 30	J. J. O'Donnell
Kells C. A. & D. S. Ltd	C. 112	Thomastown	Ballyhale 6	'Creamery Kells Kilkenny' Phone Stonyford 3	S. Power
Kilkenny C.D. S Ltd	C. 254	Tomas St , Kilkenny	Kilkenny 1	'Creamery Kilkenny' Phone Kilkenny 5	R. Norris
Kilmacow C. D. S. Ltd	C. 250	Kilmacow	Kilmacow 2.5	'Creamery Kilmacow' Phone Kilmacow 7115	D. Roche
Kilmanagh C. D. S. Ltd	C. 111	Kilmanagh, Callen	Kilkenny 10	'Creamery Kilmanagh' Phone Kilmanagh 2	F. J. McCluskey
Muckalee C. D. S. Ltd	C.141	Ballyfoyle	Kilkenny 10	'Creamery Muckalee, Ballyfoyle' Phone Muckalee Ballyfoyle 4	R. Brennan
Mullinavat C. D. S. Ltd	C. 109	Near Waterford	Mullinavat	'Creamery Mullinavat' Phone Mullinavat 3	J. Duggan
Nore Valley C. C. Ltd	C. 122	Thomastown	Thomastown 1	'Creamery Thomastown' Phone Thomastown 11	D. Ryan
Piltown C. A. & D. S. Ltd	C. 278	Piltown	Fiddown 1	'Creamery Piltown' Phone Fiddown 3	W. J. J. Sherlock BSc
Tullaroan Co-op Cry. Ltd	C. 329	Tulloran, Freshford	Kilkenny 10	'Creamery Tullaroan' Phone Tullaroan 3	N. Purcell
Windgap C.A. & D. S. Ltd	C. 184	Windgap, Thomastown	Carrick-on-Suir 8	'Creamery Windgap' Phone Windgap 3	E. Horgan

Co Laois

Name of Creamery & Owners	DP Act 1924 Reg. No	Post Town	Miles to Nearest Railway Station	Telephone No Telegraphic Address	Name of Manager
Donaghmore C.C. Ltd	C. 348	Balybrophy	Ballybrophy 1.5	'Creamery Ballybrophy' Phone Donaghmore 3	D. F. Grogan

LIST OF CENTRAL CREAMERIES (cond.)

Name of Creamery & Owners	DP Act 1924 Reg. No	Post Town	Miles to Nearest Railway Station	Telephone No Telegraphic Address	Name of Manager
Co Leitrim					
Killasnett C.A. & D. S. Ltd	C. 201	Manorhamilton	Manorhamilton	'Creamery Manorhamilton' Phone Manorhamilton 6	O. Murphy
Kiltoghert C.A. & D. S. Ltd	C. 257	Carrick-on-Shannon	Carrick-on-Shannon 3	'Creamery Kiltoghert, Leitim' Phone Leitrim 3	A.T. Hannon
Co Limerick					
Abington Co-op Cry Ltd.	C. 285	Murroe	Boher 3	'Creamery Murroe' Phone Murroe 6	J. J. Power BSc
Annacotty C.D.S. Ltd	C. 136	Lisnagry	Killonan	'Co-op Creamery Annacotty –Limerick' Phone Limerick 1209	J. McGrath
Ardagh C.D.S. Ltd	C. 109	Ardagh	Ardagh	'Creamery Ardagh, Limerick' Phone Ardagh 3	J. Fullam
Askeaton C.C. Ltd.	C. 350	Athea	Kilmorna 3	'Creamery Athea ' Phone Athea 3	P.J. Mullane
Ballyagran Co-op Cry. Ltd	C. 143	Kilmallock	Charleville 8	'Creamery Ballyagran, Charleville' Phone Ballyagran 2	M. Murphy
Ballyhahill C.D.S. Ltd	C. 231	Ballyhahill	Foynes 7	'Creamery Ballyhahill	J. O'Shaughnessy
Belville Deel Bridge C.D.S. Ltd	C. 135	Kilmeedy, Newcastlewest	Newcastlewest 7	'Creamery, Belville,, Kilmeedy' Phone Kilmeedy 3	J. Sheehan
Black Abbey C.A. & D. S. Ltd	C. 239	Adare	Adare 1	'Creamery Adare' Phone Adare 17	J.G. Casey
Bruree C.D.S. Ltd	C. 265	Bruree	Bruree 1	'Co-operative Bruree' Phone Bruree 4	M. O'Mahony
Cahirconlish C. C. Ltd	C. 214	Cahirconlish	Limerick 9	'Creamery Cahirconlish' Phone Cahirconlish 3	P. O'Brien

LIST OF CENTRAL CREAMERIES (cond.)

Name of Creamery & Owners	DP Act 1924 Reg. No	Post Town	Miles to Nearest Railway Station	Telephone No Telegraphic Address	Name of Manager
Cappamore C.A.& D.S. Ltd	C. 227	Cappamore	Dromkeen 3	'Creamery Cappamore' Phone Cappamore 3	T.McCarthy
Castlemahon C.D.S. Ltd	C. 158	Castlemahon, Newcastlewest	Newcastlewest 3	'Creamery Castlemahon' Phone Castlemahon 3	B. McEnery
Condensed Milk Co.Ltd	C.	Lansdowne, Limerick	Limerick	'Cleeve, Limerick' Phone Limerick 186-196	D Corkery MSc.
Clouncagh C.D.S. Ltd	C. 138	Ballingarry	Rathkeale 4	'Creamery, Clouncagh, Knockaderry' Phone Knockaderry 3	T.McDonnell
Drombanna Co-op Cry. Ltd	C. 264	Four Elms, Near Limerick	Limerick 3	'Drombanna Cry. Limerick Phone Ballysimon 3	E.O'Farrell
Dromkeen C.D.S. Ltd	C. 185	Cloverfield, Pallasgreen	Dromkeen 2	'Creamery Dromkeen' Phone Dromkeen 2	Domnall De Barra
Devon Road Co-op Creamery Ltd	C. 171	Templeglantine	Devon Road	'Creamery Devon Road, Templeglantine' Phone Templeglantine 3	T. J. Kelleher
Effin C.D.S. Ltd	C. 233	Kilmallock	Knocklong 2	'Creamery Effin' Phone Charleville 209	M. P. Hartnett
Fealebridge C.D.S. Ltd	C. 306	Abbeyfeale	Abbeyfeale 3	'Fealebridge Cry. Abbeyfeale' Phone Abbeyfeale 7	P. Elliott P.C.
Feenagh C.A.& D.S. Ltd	C. 204	Charleville	Charleville 10	'Creamery Feenagh' Phone Feenagh 2	J. Reidy
Garryspillane C.D.S. Ltd	C. 331	Kilmallock	Knocklong 2	'Garryspillane Creamery Knocklong' Phone Knocklong 9	J. Brickley BSc.
Glenwilliam C.D.S. Ltd	C. 268	Ballingarry	Rathkeale 5	'Glenwilliam Dairy, Ballingarry, Limerick' Phone Ballingarry 2	J. F. Benson
Glin C.A.& D.S. Ltd	C. 308	Glin	Foynes 9	'Creamery Glin' Phone Glin 6	M. J. O'Connor P.C.
Granagh C.D.S. Ltd	C. 110	Ballingarry	Croom 5	'Creamery Granagh Croom' Phone Croom 12	M. McMahon
Greybridge C.D.S.Ltd	C. 299	Meanus, Kilmallock	Croom 4	'Creamery Greybridge Croom' Phone Croom 4	M. O'Brien
Herbertstown C.A.& D.S. Ltd	C. 101	Herbertstown	Knocklong 7	'Creamery Herbertstown' Phone Herbertstown 2	L. McGrath
Hospital C.D.S. Ltd	C. 218	Hospital, Knocklong	Knocklong 3	'Co-operative Creamery Hospital'	B.J. O'Neill BSc
Kantoher C.A.& D.S. Ltd	C. 297	Ballaugh	Newcastlewest 7	'Ballagh Cry.,Charleville' Phone Ballagh 3	Denis Ward

LIST OF CENTRAL CREAMERIES (cond.)

Name of Creamery & Owners	DP Act 1924 Reg. No	Post Town	Miles to Nearest Railway Station	Telephone No Telegraphic Address	Name of Manager
Kildimo C.D.S. Ltd	C. 124	Kildimo	Adare 8	'Creamery Kildomo Palliskenry	Patrick Ryan
Kilfinny C.A.& D.S.Ltd	C. 129	Kilfinny,Adare	Croom 4	'Creamery Kilfinny,Croom' Phone Croom 5	N. P. Stephens
Klmallock Co-op Cry. Ltd	C. 332	Kilmallock	Kilmallock	'Co-op Cry. Kilmallock' Phone Kilmallock 15	M. J. Houlihan
Kilteely Co-op Cry, Society Ltd	C. 279	Kilteely Pallasgreen	Pallas 5	'Creamery Kilteely Phone Kilteely 1	P.W. King
Knocklong (C. M. Co)	C. 300	Knocklong	Knocklong	'Cleeve Knocklong'	J. Daly
Mount Collins C.D.S. Ltd	C. 126	Munt Collins Abbeyfeale	Abbeyfeale 8	'Creamery Mountcollins Brosna'	F. T. Moran
Newcastlewest C.D.S. Ltd	C. 263	Newcastlewest	Newcastlewest	'Creamery, Newastlewest' Phone Newcastlewest 5	J. Ryan
Oola Co-op. Creamery Ltd	C. 276	Oola, Tipperary	Oola	'Creamery Oola' Phone Oola 3	Sean Nash
Rathkeale C.D.S. Ltd.	C. 267	Rathkeale	Rathkeale	'Co-operative Cry. Rathkeale' Phone Rathkeale 8	M. O'Brien
Sarsfield C.A.&D.S.Ltd	C. 284	Templebredin,Pallasgreen	Pallasgreen 4	'Creamery , Ballydoolis' Phone Emly 3	J. Sheehy
Shanagolden C. D.S. Ltd	C. 105	Shanagolden	Foynes 3	'Creamery Shanagolden' Phone Shanagolden 3	P. O'Connell BSc
Toher C.D.S. Ltd	C. 288	Doon	Pallas 5	'Toher Creamery ,|Doon' Phone Doon 12	R. J. Walsh
Tournafulla Co-op Cry Ltd.	C. 103	Tournafulla, Newcastlewest	Devon Road 6	'Co-operative Tournafulla' Phone Tournafulla 3	W. W. Curtin
Co Monaghan Clones C. A. & D. S. Ltd	C.	Clones	Clones	'Creamery Clones' Phone Clones 21	H. H. Bustard
Lough Egish C.D.S. Ltd	C. 323	Castleblaney	Castleblaney 5	'Creamery Tullynahinera' Phone Tullynahinera 2	J. Daly
Town of Monaghan C.A.& D.S. Ltd	C. 194	Coolshannagh , Monaghan	Monaghan	'Creamery, Monaghan' Phone Monaghan 35	J. J. O'Donnell

LIST OF CENTRAL CREAMERIES (cond.)

Name of Creamery & Owners	DP Act 1924 Reg. No	Post Town	Miles to Nearest Railway Station	Telephone No Telegraphic Address	Name of Manager
Co. Roscommon					
Carnadoe C.A.& D.S. Ltd	C.	Kilmore, Carrick-on-Shannon	Drumsna 4	'Cry, Kilmore, Drumsna'	**Vacant**
Co. Sligo					
Achonry C.A.& D.S. Ltd	C. 228	Achonry, Ballymote.	Carrowmore 2.5	'Achonry, Cry, Tubbercurry' Phone Tubbercurry 12	**T. O'Mahony**
Ballinafull C.A.& D.S. Ltd	C. 231	Ballinafull	Sligo 10	'Creamery Ballinafull' Phone Ballinafull 4	**J. F. O'Hart**
Ballintrillick C.D.S. Ltd	C. 286	Cliftoney	Bundoran 10	'Creamery Cliftoney'	**J. Keogh**
Drumcliffe C.a.& D.S. Ltd	C. 230	Drumcliffe, Sligo	Sligo 6	'Creamery Drumcliffe' Phone Doumcliffe 3	**Joseph Curry**
Gurteen C.A.& D.S. Ltd	C. 179	Gurteen Via Boyle	Kilfree 4 Boyle 7	'Creamery Gurteen ,Sligo' Phone Gurteen 7	**M. Horan BSc** **Patrick Hughes**
Kilmactranny C.A.7 D.S. Ltd	C. 202	Tubbercurry	Tubbercurry	'Creamery Kilmactranny' Phone Ballyfarnon 3	**S. O'Mearlain**
Rathscanlon C.C. Ltd	C. 355	Riverstown, Ballymote	Collooney 6	'Creamery Tubbercurry' 'Creamery Riverstown' Phone Riverstown 3	**C. Lyons**
Riverstown C.A.& D.S. Ltd	C. 181				
Co Tipperary					
Ballingarry C.A.&D.S. Ltd	C. 330	Ballingarry Thurles	Laffins Bridge 7	' Cry, Ballingarry, Thurles' Phone Ballingarry 3	**M. Kealy**
Ballypatrick C.D.S. Ltd	C. 192	Ballypatrick, Clonmel	Kiilsheelan 3	'Creamery Ballypatrick' Phone Ballypatrick 2	**M. J. Butler**
Ballywilliam C.D.S. Ltd	C. 321	Nenagh	Nenagh	'Cry, Ballywilliam, Nenagh' Phone Nenagh 347	**A. Murray**
Boherlahan C. A & D.S. Ltd	C. 198	Ardmayle, Thurles	Goolds Cross 3	'Cry, Ardmoyle, Goolds Cross' Phone Goolds Cross 2	**P. Harrington**
Borrisoleigh C.D.S. Ltd	C. 165	Borrisoleigh	Templemore 6	' Creamery Borrisoleigh' Phone Borrisoleigh 4	**T. Ryan**

LIST OF CENTRAL CREAMERIES (cond.)

Name of Creamery & Owners	DP Act 1924 Reg. No	Post Town	Miles to Nearest Railway Station	Telephone No Telegraphic Address	Name of Manager
Centenary C.D.S. Ltd	C, 215	Ballyduff Thurles	Thurles 5	'Centenary Thurles' Phone Littleton 3	D. O'Mahony
Clonmel and Newcastle C.C. Ltd	C. 237	Suir Island, Clonmel	Clonmel	'Creamery Clonmel' Phone Clonmel 2	J. Deasy
Coolmoyne and Fethard C.C. Ltd.	C. 187	Coolmoyne, Fethard	Fethard 4	'Coolmoyne,Creamery, Fethard,Tipperary' Phone Fethard 6	Andrew Kearney
Drangan C.C.Ltd	C. 217	Drangan, Thurles	Fethard 8	'Creamery Drangan' Phone Drangan 5	P. Sugrue
Drombane C.D.S. Ltd	C. 312	Drombane, Thurles	Thurles 8	'[Dairy, Drombane, Thurles' Phone Drombane 3	J. Lanigan
Fennor C.A. & D.S. Ltd	C. 121	Gortnahoe, Thurles	Thurles 12	'Dairy, Gortnahoe' Phone Gortnahoe 4	J. Campion
Grangemokler C.D. S. Ltd	C. 148	Carrig-on-Suir	Carrin-on Suir 9	'Co-operation Nine-mile-House' Phone Nine-mile-House 3	D. Kelleher
Hollyford C.A.& D. S. Ltd	C. 282	Hollyford Tipperary	Dundrum 9	'Creamery Hollyford' Phone Hollyford 3	F. Blackwell
Knockavardagh C.D.S. Ltd	C. 261	Killenaule, Thurles	Laffanbridge 3	'Co-operative Killenaule' Phone Killenaule 5	O. P. O'Neill
Kilross C.A.& D. S. Ltd.	C. 175	Rathkea, Tipperary	Tipperary 5	'Kilross Creamery, Lattin' Phone Lattin 3	M. Ryan
Mullinahone C.D.S. Ltd	C. 119	Mullinahone, Thurles	Carrig-on-Suir 12	'Co-operative, Mullinahone' Phone Mullinahone 3	D. Foley BSc
Nenagh Co-op Creamery Ltd	C. 253	Nenagh	Nenagh	'Creamery Nenagh' Phone Nenagh 4	T. Ryan
Newport C.A. & D. S. Ltd	C. 125	Near Limerick	Limerick 10	'Cry. Newport,Limerick' Phone Newport 3	J. Lacey
Outrath C.D.S. Ltd	C. 180	New Inn, Cahir	Cahir 4	'Cry, New inn, Cahir' Phone New Inn 3	D. Kerins
Solohead C.A.& D.S. Ltd	C. 271	Limerick Junction	Limerick Junction 2	'Solohear Cry, limerick Junction' Phone Limerick Junction 2	J. Blackwell
Suirvale C.A.& D.S. Ltd	C.	Cahir	Cahir	'Creamery Cahir' Phone Cahir 209	J. O'Donovan
Thurles C.A.& D. S. Ltd	C. 188	Thurles	Thurles	' Creamery Thurles' Phone Thurles 15	John Cleary
Tipperary Co-op Cry Ltd	C. 173	Tipperary	Tipperary	'Co-op Creamery, Tipperary' Phone Tipperary 21leeve,	E. O'Callaghan
Tipperery (C.M. Co)	C. 342	Tipperary	Tipperary	'Cleeve, Tipperary' Tel, 18	D. O'Connell
Uperchurch C.A.& D.S.	C. 149	Upperchurch Thurles	Thurles	'Creamery Upperchurch' Phone Upperchurch 3	Joseph Fay

LIST OF CENTRAL CREAMERIES (cond.)

Name of Creamery & Owners	DP Act 1924 Reg. No	Post Town	Miles to Nearest Railway Station	Telephone No Telegraphic Address	Name of Manager
Co Waterford					
Dungarvan Co-op Cry,Ltd	C. 255	Dungarvan	Dungarvan	'Co-operate Dungarvan' Phone Dungarvan 3	J. Foley BSc
Gaultier C.D.S. Ltd	C. 255	Dunmore East	Waterford	'Creamery, Gaultier' Phone Dunmore East 7324	B. Mulhern
Kilmeaden C.C.Ltd.	C. 243	Waterford	Kilmeaden	'Creamery, Kilmeaden' Phone Kilmeaden 6	D. Murphy
Knockmeal C.D.S. Ltd	C. 150	Ballinamult via Clonmel	C appagh 9	'Creamery, Ballinamult' Phone Ballinamult 2	T. Callanan
Millvale Co-op. Creanery Ltd	C. 294	Millvale,C arrig-on- Suir	Carrig-on-Suir 2	'Co-operative, Millvale, Carrig-on-Suir' Phone Carrig-on-Suir 2	J.O'Donoghue
Co Wexford					
Inch C.D.S.Ltd	C. 200	Inch	Inch	'Creamery, Inch, Gorey'	G. W. Kinley

LIST OF AUXILIARY CREAMERIES IN IRELAND

Name of Creamery & Owners	Post Town	Miles to Nearest Railway Station	Telephone No Telegraphic Address	Name of Manager
Co Cavan				
Ardagh (Killeshandra C.A.&D.S.Ltd)	Arva	Arva Road 4	'Ardagh Creamery Arva'	T. Brady
Ardlogher (Killeshandra)	Bulturbet	Ballyconnell 5	'Killeshandra 4	J. McDermott
Belturbet C.D.S.(Indept-Killeshandra)	Belturbet	Belturbet	'Creamery Belturbet'	P. O'Reilly
Billis C.C. Ltd (indept – Annagelliffe C.D.S.)	Billis, Virginia	Virginia Rd. 8	'Creamery, Billis, Virginia'	F. Reilly
Blacklion (KillasnettC.D.S.Ltd)	Blacklion	Belcoo & Blacklion	'Creamery Blacklion'	B Smith
Bunnoe C.C. Ltd (Indept -Annagelliffe C.D.S.)	Bunnoe, Lisboduff, Coothill	Coothill 7	Bunnoe Creamery, Tullavin 6	G. Smith
Butlersbridge (Killeshandra C.A.& D.S. Ltd)	Butlersbridge	Ballyhaise 3	'Creamery, Butlersbridge'	P Gaffney
Carrigan (Killeshandra)	Ballinagh	Drumhowna 4	Ballinagh P.O.	J. Crotty
Carrickallen Creamery (Indept—Annagelliffe)	Mountain Lodge,Coothill	Coothill 9	'Creamery. Carrickallen, Stradone'	P. J. Brennan
Corraghoe C.D.S.(Indept –Annagelliffe)	Stradone	Cavan 6	Corraghoe Cry, Stradone'	A. Smith
Crossdoney (Killeshandra)	Crossdoney	Crossdoney	Crossdoney PO	F. King
Crosskeys Annagelliffe C.D.S.)	Crosskeys	Cavan 6	'Crosskeys Creamery,Ballyjamesduff''	T. Brady
Dromcrow C.D.S (Indept-Annagelliffe)	Carrigboy	Cavan 4	Creamery Dromcrow'	J. McCabe
Gortermore (Indept – Killeshandra)	Moyne	Killeshandra	'Creamery Gortormore'	M. Smith
GrousehallC.A.& D.S. (Indept- Annagelliffe)	Loughduff	Dromhowna	Ballinagh PO 5	P. Galligan
Kill C.D.S. (Indept-Annagelliffe)	Tullyvin,Coothill	Coothill 4	Tullivin PO	J. H. Carey
Lossett (Killeshandra)	Corlesmore	Crossdoney 4	Ballinagh PO 5	J. J. Duighnan
Maudabawn C.D.S. Ltd (Indept- Lough Egish)	Maudabawn, Coothill	Coothill 3.5	'Creamery, Maudabawn, Coothill'	H. Mc Bride

LIST OF AUXILIARY CREAMERIES IN IRELAND (Continued)

Name of Creamery & Owners	Post Town	Miles to Nearest Railway Station	Telephone No Telegraphic Address	Name of Manager
Miltown (Killeshandra)	Milltown	Belturbet 3	Belturbet PO 3	B. Wilson
Poles Co-Op Creamery (Indept – Annagelliffe)	Poles	Cavan 3.5	Stradone PO 3	C. O'Mahony
Redhills C.A.& D.S. Ltd (Indept – Annagelliffe)	Redhills	Redhills	'Creamery Redhills'	C.Lynch
SwanlinbarC.A.& D.S. Ltd Indept- Killeshandra)	Swanlinbar	Bawnboy Road 8	'Creamery Swanlinbar'	P. J. McHugh
Templeport C.A.& D.S. Ltd (Indept -)	Templeport, Bawnboy	Bawnboy Road	'Creamery Bawnboy'	J. McManus
Tomkin Road (Killeshandra)	Domasladdy,Belturbet	Tomkin Rd.	Belturbet PO 3.5	P. Reilly

Co Carlow

Crettyard (Castlecomer C.D.S.)	Crettyard	Castlecomer 4	'Creamery,Crettyard, Carlow'	J. B. McKenna

Co Clare

Annagerragh (W. Clared.D. Co)	Mullagh, Ennis	Kilrush 9	Craggaknock PO 1.5	B O'Kelly
Ardanacrusha (Drombanna C.D.S.)	Parteen, Limerick	Limerick 3.5	'Parteen, Limerick'r	T. Murphy
Ballinacarra (N. Clare D.D. Co)	Kilfenora	Enistymon 4	'Ballinacarra Creamery, Kilfenora'	J. O'Connor
Bella Cross (W. Clare DDC)	Killenaugh, Carrigahiolt.	Kilkee 5	'Creamery, Carrigaholt'	W. Enright
Bridgetown Co-op Creamery (Indept – Newport CDS)	O'Briens Bridge	Castleconnell 3	'Clonlara, Limerick'	T. Sexton
Blackweir (W. Clare DDC)	Lisdeen	Kilkee	'Creamery.Blackweir, Kilkee'	J. Quirke
Clondegad (W. Clare DDC)	Ballynacally, Ennis	Clarecastle 7	Ballynacally PO 1	J. Considine P.C.
Cooraclare (W.ClareDDC)	Coolaclare, Ennis	Kilrush 6	Cooraclare PO	D.Horgan
Coore (N. Clare DDC)	Milltown-Malbay	Milltown-Malbay 3.5	Mullagh PO 3.5	C.Curtin
Cranny (W. Clare DDC)	Cranny	Kilrush 14	Cranny PO	T. Ayres

191

LIST OF AUXILIARY CREAMERIES IN IRELAND (Continued)

Name of Creamery & Owners	Post Town	Miles to Nearest Railway Station	Telephone No Telegraphic Address	Name of Manager
Darragh (N. Clare DDC)	Ennis	Ennis 4	'Darragh Creamery, Ennis'	John K. Tobin
Derrylough (W. Clare DDC)	Killimer	Kilrush 3	Killimer PO 1	H. Upton
Doolin (N. Clare DDC)	Doolin, Ennis	Lisdoonvarna 7	Lisdoonvarna PO 2.5	M. B. Cusack
Doonaha (W. Clare DDC)	Doonaha , Kilkee	Kilkee 3	Kilkee PO 3	J. J. Herlihy
Feakle (E. Clare DDC)	Feakle	Limerick 25	Feakle PO	P. J. Sheahan
Honan's Bridge (N. Clare DDC)	Miltown	Miltown 1	'Honan's Bridge Creamery, Miltown'	K. Scanlon
Inagh (N. Clare DDC)	Ennis	Ennistymon 7	Inagh , Ennis	J. O'Connor
Kilbaha (W. Clare DDC)	Kilbaha, Kilkee	Kilkee 14	Carrigaholt PO 7	M. Calnan
Kildysart W. Clare DDC)	Kildysart, Ennis	Kilrush 20	Kildysart PO 1	P. McCarthy
Killaloe (Annacotty C.D.S. Ltd)	Killaloe	Killaloe	'Creamery, Killaloe'	J. Fitzgerald
Kilmihil (W. Clare DDC)	Kilmihill	Kilmihill	Kilmihill PO	P. Galvin
Kilmurray McMahon (. Clare DDC)	Kilmurray McMahon, Ennis	Kilrush 10	Kilmurray PO	F. Browne
Kilmaley (N. Clare DDC)	Ennis	Ennis 5	'Kilmaley, Creamery, Ennis,	Patk. Tobin
Kilnamona (N. Clare DDC)	Ennis	Ennis 3	'Kilnamona Creamery, Ennis'	F. Corey
Labasheeda (W. Clare DDC)	Labasheeda	Ennis 13	Labasheeda PO	B. Garvey
Liscannor (N. Clare DDC)	Lahinch	Lahhinch 3	Liscannor PO	A. Clair
Lissecasey (W. Clare DDC)	Lissecasey, Ennis	Ennis 11	Lissecasey, Ennis	S. Culligan
Moy (N. Clare DDC)	Lahinch	Lahinch 3	'Moy Creamery, Lahinch'	J. J. Shine
Newmarket-on-Fergus (Bunratty C.D.S.)	Newmarket-on-Fergus	Ballycar 1.5	Newmarket-on-Fergus	P. Ahern
Power's Cross (W. Clare DDC)	Doonbeg	Doonbeg 2	Doonbeg PO	J. Walsh
Smithstown (N. Clare DDC)	Kilshanny, Ennis	Ennistymon 5	'Creamery, Smithstown, Kilshanny'	C. Keating BSc
Tulla (E. Clare DDC)	Tulla	Limerick 18	Tulla 1	Martin Hoyne
Whitegate (E. Clare DDC)	Whitegate	Limerick 25	\Whitegate 1	D. Moore

Co Cork

Name of Creamery & Owners	Post Town	Miles to Nearest Railway Station	Telephone No Telegraphic Address	Name of Manager
Ahadillane (Ballyclough CDS)	Ahadillane,, Donoughmore	Rathduff 6	'Creamery Ahsdillane, Donoughmore'	T. O'Callaghan

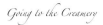

LIST OF AUXILIARY CREAMERIES IN IRELAND (Continued)

Name of Creamery & Owners	Post Town	Miles to Nearest Railway Station	Telephone No Telegraphic Address	Name of Manager
Adrigole (Drinagh CC)	Adrigole, Skibbereen	Skibbereen 4	'Adrigole Creamery, Skibbereen' Phone Leap 14	A. Jagoe
Araglin (Mitchelstown CC)	Kilworth	Fermoy 10	'Cry, Araglin Kilworth'	J. Peters
Ardfield (Lisavard CC)	Clonakilty	Clonakilty	Rathbarry PO	J. Scully
Aghabullogue (Coachford DDC)	Aghabullogue, Coachford	Peake 2.5	'Creamery, Aghabullogue, Coachford'	T. Geaney
Abuane (Kilcorney CDS)	Millstreet	Millstreet 5	Millstreet 3.5	J. Creedon
Ballinadee (Bandon CDS)	Ballinadee, Bandon	Bandon 6	Bandon	Jas. Holland
Ballinascarthy (Lisavard CC)	Clonakilty	Ballinascarthy	Clonakilty	J. Spillane
Ballindangan (Mitchelstown CC)	Ballindangan	Ballindangan	Mitchelstown 4	J. J. Rea
Ballinhassig C.C. Ltd (Indept- UCC)	Ballinhassig	Ballinhassig 1	'Creamery Ballinhassig' Phone Ballinhassig 5	Liam Stack
Ballincurrig (Castlelyons CC)	Ballincurring, Leamlara	Midleton 7	'Ballincurring Cry., Midleton'	J. McSweeney
Ballycummer (Lisavard CDS)	Clonakilty	Clonakilty 4	Clonakilty 4	M. Dineen
Ballinamona (Ballyclough CDS)	Shanballymore, Mallow	Castletownroche 6	Castletownroche 6	T. Mannix
Ballymakeera (Clondrohid)	Ballymakeera, Macroom	Macroom 9	'Cry, Ballymakeera, Macroom '	John Shine
Ballyclough C.D.S.	Mallow	Mallow 6	'Creamery Ballyclough'	B. O'Keeffe
Ballybahallow (Fremount DS)	Freemount	Kanturk 4	Freemount	J.J. O'Sullivan
Ballydaly (Rathmore DDC)	Milllstreet	Millstreet 5	Millstreet	D. Murphy
Ballyhea (Shandrum CDS)	Charleville	Charleville 4	Ballyhea	J. Herbert
Ballyhooley (Mitchelstown CC)	Mallow	Ballyhooley	Ballyhooley	P. Murphy
Ballingeary (Terelton NDC)	Ballingeary	Ballingeary	'Cry., Ballingeary Macroom'	J. Corkery
Ballinlough (Drinagh CC)	Leap	Skibbereen 5	Leap	D. Hurley
Ballyrichard (Imokilly CC)	Midleton	Midleton	'Ballyrichard Creamery, Midleton'	W. E. O'Driscoll
Ballinspittle (Barryroe CC)	Ballinspittle, Kilsale	Kinsale	'Creamery Ballinspttle'	D. Sexton

193

LIST OF AUXILIARY CREAMERIES IN IRELAND (Continued)

Name of Creamery & Owners	Post Town	Miles to Nearest Railway Station	Telephone No Telegraphic Address	Name of Manager
Banagh (North –Cork CC)	Castlemagner, Kanturk	Kanturk 3	Kanturk	M. O'Sullivan
Bantry (Drinagh CC)	Bantry	Bantry	'Creamery Bantry' Tel 97	D. Keohane
Ballyhoulihan (North-Cork CC)	Ballyhoulihan, Kanturk	Kanturk 3	Kanturk	J. O'Driscoll
Bawnmore (Clondrohid CC)	Bawnmore, Macroom	Macroom 4	'Creamery, Bawnmore, Macroom'	N. Murphy
Bengour (Terelton NDC)	Castletown-Kinnagh, Enniskeane	Crookstown 8	……………..	Sean Curtin
Bere Island (Castletownbere CC)	Castletownbere	Castletownbere	……………………	M. O'Leary
Berrings (Coachford DDC)	Berrings	Cloghroe 3	'Creamery Berrings, Cork'	P. P. Healy
Buttevant (Ballyclough CDS)	Buttevant	Buttevant	Buttevant	J. Walsh
Carhuvouler (Lisavard CDS)	Ballineen	Ballineen	Ballineen	Jas. McCarthy
Carriganima (Clondrohid CDS)	Macroom	Macroom 7	Macroom	J. Leahy
Carrigaline CDS Ltd (Indept- UCC)	Carrigaline	Carrigaline 5.5	'Creamery Carrigaline' Tel. Carrigaline 8	P. Silke
Carrignavar (Ballyclough CDS)	Carrignavar	Kilbarry 6	'Creamery Carrignavar'	B. Harte
Castlecor (North Cork CC)	Castlecor, Kanturk	Kanturk 4	'Castlecor, Co. Cork'	T. Cusack
Castle Donovan (Drinagh CC)	Drimoleague	Drimoleague 3.5	'Creamery Castle Donovan, Tel. Drimoleague 18	J. O'Driscoll
Castlehaven (Drinagh CC)	Skibbereen	Skibbereen 4	Skibbereen , 4. Tel. Castletownshend 12	J. O'Donovan
Castletownroche (Ballyclough CC)	Castletownroche	Castletownroche 3	Castletownroche	T. F. Mannix
Caum (Coachford NDC)	Killinardrish	Coachford 4	Coachford 4	E. Forde
Charleville (Shandrum CDS)	Charleville	Charleville 1	'Creamery Charleville'	J. Twomey
Churhtown (Ballyclough CC)	Churchtown, Mallow	Buttevant 1	'Dairy, Churchtown, Buttevant'	M. J. Ahern
Churchcross (West Cork Creameries)	Skibbereen	Skibbereen 4	Skibbereen 4	G. O'Mahoney

LIST OF AUXILIARY CREAMERIES IN IRELAND (Continued)

Name of Creamery & Owners	Post Town	Miles to Nearest Railway Station	Telephone No Telegraphic Address	Name of Manager
Clohane (Drinagh CC)	Skibbereen	Skibbereen 4	'Clohane Creamery' Tel. Skibbereen 83	R. J. Patterson
Clonakilty (Lisavard CDS)	Clonakilty	Clonakilty	'Creamery Clonakilty' Tel. Clonakilty 15	Mce. Mc Carthy
Colomane (Drinagh CC)	Bantry	Bantry 5	Bantry; Tel Bantry 23	B. Begley
Cononagh (Drinagh CC)	Leap	Skibbereen 8	'Creamery Cononagh, Leap ' Tel. Leap 11	P. O'Donovan
Conna (Castlelyons CDS)	Conna	Ballyduff 5	'Creamery Conna'	T. Manton
Corroghurm (Mitchelstown CC)	Mitchelstown	Mitchelstown 6	Co-op Cry, Corroghurm Mitchelstowmn'	Thomas Kelly
Courtbrack (Ballyclough CDS)	Blarney	Blarney	'Cry, Courtbrack, Blarney	T. Twomey
Coolea (Clondrohid CDS)	Ballyvourney	Macroom 13	Ballymakeera 3	W. Wiseman
Crossbarry (Bandon CDS)	Upton	Kinsale Junction	'Creamery Crossbarry, Innishannon'	B. Dempsey
Cullen (North Cork CDS)	Millstreet	Millstreet 4	Millstreet 4	J. P. O'Riordan
Cummer (Newmarket CDS)	Meelin PO, Newmarket	Newmarket 5	'Cummer Creamery Meelin'	W. Cuddihy
Darrara (Barryroe CC)	Clonakilty	Clonakilty 3	Clonakilty	W. O'Mahony
Dreenybridge (West Cork Creameries)	Skibbereen	Madore 1	Skibbereen	T. Hourihane
Dromina (Milford)	Drimina, Charleville	Charleville 7	Tel. Dromina 7	D. Leahy
Derrygrea (Drinagh CC)	Drimoleague	Drimoleague 1	Tel. Drimoleague 9	D. O'Driscoll
Doneraile (Ballyclough CDS)	Doneraile	Buttevant 5	Doneraile	J. Lyons
Donoughmore (Ballyclough CDS)	Donoughmore	Firmount	'Creamery Donoghmore'	M. Fitzgibbon
Dripsey (Coachford NDC)	Dripsey	Cork	Coachford	D. O'Leary
Dunmanway (Drinagh CC)	Dunmanway	Dunmanway	'Creamery Dunmanway' Tel. Dunmanway 32	John Dinneen
Durras (Drinagh CC)	Durras	Durras 4	'Creamery Durras' Tel. Durras 5	D. Hurley
Enniskeane (Bandon CDS)	Enniskeane	Enniskeane	Enniskeane	J. J. O'Brien
Glanworth (Mitchelstown CC)	Glanworth	Glanworth	'Creamery Glanworth'	T. O'Brien
Glandore (Lisavard CDS)	Skibbereen	Skibbereen 12	'Creamery Glandore'	J. J. O'Brien
Glenville (Castlelyons CDS)	Glenville, Fermoy	Fermoy 13	'Glenville Cry, Fermoy'	C. McCarthy

Name of Creamery & Owners	Post Town	Miles to Nearest Railway Station	Telephone No Telegraphic Address	Name of Manager
Glashakinleen (Newmarket CDS)	Newmarket	Newmarket 4	Newmarket	P. O'Driscoll
Glen. South (Nth. Cork Co-op)	Lyre, Banteer	Banteer 4	Banteer	C. Walsh
Gurteenakilla (West Cork Creameries)	Ballydehob	Skibbereen 13	Ballydehob	P. McCarthy
Hawthorn (Drinagh CC)	Drimoleague	Drimoleague 2	Tel. Drimoleague 13	H. Collins
Imokilly C.C.S.Ltd (Indept UCC Cork)	Mogeely	Mogeely	'Creamery Mogeely' Tel Castlemartyr 2	J. Holland
Inchigeela (Terelton NDC)	Inchigeela	Macroom 10	'Creamery Inchigeela'	R. Looney
Inchy Bridge (Barryroe CDS)	Timoleague	Timoleague 2	'Creamery Inchy Bridge, Timoleague'	W. Finn
Kealkil (Drinagh CC)	Kealkil, Bantry	Bantry 6	'Creamery Kealkil, Bantry' Tel. Kealkil 3	C. J. Hanley
Kilbehenny (Mitchelstown CC)	Mitchlstown	Mitchelstown 4	Kilbehenny	P. Quish
Kilbrittain (Barryroe CDS)	Bandon	Timoleague 3.5	'Co-op Kilbrittain'	M. McCarthy
Kilcoe (West Cork Creameries)	Skibbereen	Kilcoe	Skibbereen	J. Sheehan
Kilcoleman (Coachford NDC)	Coachford	Peake	'Cry, Kilcoleman, Coachford'	M. Roche
Kilcrohane (Drinagh CC)	Bantry	Bantry 10	'Kilcrohane Creamery, Bantry' Tel. Kilcrohane 3	J. Lane
Kildorrery (Mitchelston CC)	Kildorrery	Glanwoeth 6	Tel. Kildorrery 3	D Broderick
Kilworth (Mitchelstown CC)	Fermoy	Fermoy 3	Kilworth	P. O'Donoghue
Kilmeen (Drinagh CC)	Rossmore, Clonalilty	Ballinneen 7	'Rossmre, Clonakilty' Tel Rossmore 3	M. O'Mahoney
Kinsale (Bandon CDS)	Kinsale	Ballinhassig 9	'Creamery Kinsale'	J. F. Tobin
Kilnamartyra (Clondrohid CC)	Kilnamartyra, Macroom	Macroom 6	'Creamery Kilnamartyra. Ballymakeera'	C. T. Murray
Killavullen (Ballyclough CDS)	Mallow	Killavullen 1	Killavullen, Mallow	G. Fitzgerald
Killowen (Terelton NDC)	Killowen, Bandon	Clonakilty Junction 2	'Killowen Dairy, Bandon'	T. A. O'Mahoney

Name of Creamery & Owners	Post Town	Miles to Nearest Railway Station	Telephone No Telegraphic Address	Name of Manager
Kiskeam (Newmarket CDS)	Kiskeam	Newmarket 7	Meelin, Newmarket'	D. J. Casey
Knockscovane (Freemount Dairy Soc.)	Meelin, Newmarket	Newmarket 6		M. O'Riordan
Knockraha (U. C. Cork)	Knockraha, Glanmire	Cork 7	'Cry. Knockraha, Glanmire' Tel. Glanmire 76	T. Mc Grath
Lacka (Rathmore)	Knocknagree	Rathmore 5	Knocknagree	D. Hickey
Lake Vale (Newmarket CDS)	Ballydesmond, Banteer	Rathmore 8	'Lakevale Dairy, Ballydesmond'	D. Hickey
Lissarda (Muskerry & Lissarda Co-op Creameries)	Lissarda	Dooniskey	'Lissarda Dairy, Crookstown' Tel. Crookstown 5	John Corcoran
Liscarroll (Indept.-Freemount CDS)	Liscarroll, Mallow	Butteant 6	'Dairy Liscarroll'	T. F. Crimmins
Lismire (Newmarket CDS)	Kanturk	Kanturk 6	Kanturk	W. Riordan
Lowertown (Drinagh CC)	Schull, Skibbereen	Schull 3	Tel. Schull 5	M. P. O'Sullivan
Macroom (Coachford NDC)	Macroom	Macroom	Macroom	P.J. Healy
Manch (Lisavard CA &DS)	Ballinacarriga, Ballineen	Ballineen	'Creamery, Ballinacarriga. Ballineen'	J. J. Collins
Maulbrack (Bandon CDS)	Enniskeane	Bandon 6	Bandon	J. O'Sullivan
Mealagh (Drinagh CC)	Bantry	Bantry ^ 6	'Creamery Mealagh, Bantry'	--
Mossgrove (Terelton NDC)	Mountpleasant, Bandon	Crookstown 5	Crookstown	J. Kelleher
Mourne Abbey (Ballyclough CDS)	Mallow	Mourne Abbey	'Creanery Mourne Abbey' Tel Mallow 56	W. Egar
Park (Imokilly CDS)	Park, Youghal	Youghal 4	Youghal	D. Sweeney
Rathduff (Ballyclough CDS)	Rathduff, Grenagh	Rathduff	'Cry, Rathduff, Grenagh, Blarney'	W. Kirwan
Reenascreena (Lisavard)	Clonakilty	Clonakilty 8	Rosscarbery	--
Rosscarbery (Lisavard CDS)	Rosscarbery	Clonakilty 7	'Creamery Rosscarbery'	C. Harte
Rowells (Newmarket CDS)	Newmarket	Newmarket 6	Meelin	James McCarthy
Rusheen (Coachford NDC)	Rusheen, Killinardrish	Macroom 4	'Creamery, Rusheen, Killinardrish'	D. D. O'Mahony

LIST OF AUXILIARY CREAMERIES IN IRELAND (Continued)

Name of Creamery & Owners	Post Town	Miles to Nearest Railway Station	Telephone No Telegraphic Address	Name of Manager
Rylane (Coachford NDC)	Rylane	Peake 6	'Rylane Creamery'	M. Kelleher
St. Brendan's (Rathmore DDC)	Millstreet	Millstreet	'St. Brendan's, Millstreet'	M, Clune
Shinaugh (Terelton NDC)	Dunmanway	Ballineen 5	--	D. McDonnell
Skeagh (West Cork Creameries)	Skibbereen	Skibbereen 8	Skibbereen	D. McAuliffe
Skibbereen (West Cork Creameries)	Skibbereen	Skibbereen	Tel Skibbereen 10	J. O'Shea
Teergay (Terelton NDC)	Macroom	Macroom 7	Macroom	Daniel Creedon
Templemary (Ballyclough CDS)	Templemary, Buttevant	Buttevant 4	'Creamery, Templemary, Buttevant'	J. Noonan
Timoleague (Barryroe CDS)	Timoleague	Timoleague	Timoleague	D. P. Mehigan
Toames (Terelton NDC)	Macroom	Dooniskey 3	'Cry. Toames, Macroom'	H. J. Shine
Turreenclassagh (Boherbue CDS)	Knocknagree	Millstreet 9	Knocknagree	P. Breen
Templemartin (Muskerry & Lissarda CC)	Bandon	Bandon 7	Bandon	M. McMahon
Union Hall (Lisavard CDS)	Skibbereen	Skibbereen 6	Union Hall	D. O'Mahony
Whiddy Island (West Cork Creameries)	Bantry	Bantry	--	D. Minihane

Co Donegal

Name of Creamery & Owners	Post Town	Miles to Nearest Railway Station	Telephone No Telegraphic Address	Name of Manager
Convoy (Indept.- Lagan CDS)	Convoy	Convoy	Convoy	Vacant
Drumholm (Indept.-Belleek)	Bridgetown	Bridgetown 1	'Creamery Ballintra'	A. Dodd
Finn Valley CDS (Indept.-Lagan)	Crossroads Killygordon	Killygordon 1	'Creamery, Killygordon'	F. Reid
Kilbarron CA & DS (Indept.- Belleek)	Cashelarden, Ballyshannon	Ballyshannon 3	'Creamery, Ballyshannon'	M. O'Reilly
Pettigo (Indept.-Belleek)	Pettigo	Pettigo	'Creamery Pettigo'	J. J. Lunny
Taughboyne CA & DS (Indept.- Lagan CDS)	St. Johnston, Lifford	St. Johnston 1	'Creamery, St. Johnston'	A. Sproule
Tuppyrapp (Lagan CDS)	Raphoe	Coolaghey 1	Raphoe	S. Stephenson

LIST OF AUXILIARY CREAMERIES IN IRELAND (Continued)

Name of Creamery & Owners	Post Town	Miles to Nearest Railway Station	Telephone No Telegraphic Address	Name of Manager
Co. Kerry				
Annascaul (Dingle DDC)	Annascaul	Annascaul	--	J. Hartnett
Anabla (Rathmore DDC)	Rathmore	Rathmore	Killarney	Michael J. Daly
Ballinskelligs (Cahirciveen DDC)	Cahirciveen	Cahirciveen 9	Cahirciveen	T. O'Connell
Ballyferriter (Dingle DDC)	Dingle	Dingle 9	Ballyferriter	Peadar Dineen
Ballyhar Creamery (Castlemaine DDC)	Farranfore	Ballybrack	Farranfore	T. O'Leary
Ballyheigue (Ardfert DDC)	Ballyheigue	Ardfert 7	'Creamery Ballyheigue'	J. P. Stritch P. C.
Ballyfinane (Castlemaine DDC)	Firies	Molahifte 4	Castlemaine	J. Daly
Ballymacquinn (Ardfert DDC)	Ballymacquinn	Abbeydorney 3	Abbeydorney	L. Brosnan
Ballinascreena (Ardfert DDC)	Causeway, Tralee	Abbeydorney 11	'Prosperity, Causeway'	J. O'Connor
Ballylongford (Listowel DDC)	Ballylongford	Listowel 9	'Cry. Ballylongford'	J. V. Harte
Beauford (Castlemaine DDC)	Beauford	Killarney 8	Beauford	J. Shine
Ballymacelligott (Dicksgrove DDC)	Ballymacelligott	Killarney 8	Ballymacelligott	Seamus Byrne
Banemore (Ardfert DDC)	Ardfert	Ardfert 6	Ballyheigue	J. B. Moriarty
Bealnadeega (Rathmore DDC)	Headford, Killarney	Headford 3	Headford	M. Willis
Camp (Dingle DDC)	Camp	Castlegregory Junction	--	P. Donnelly
Causeway (Ardfert DDC)	Causeway, Tralee	Abbeydorney 5	'Creamery Causeway'	D. Brosnan
Chapeltown (Ardfert DDC)	Spa	Spa 3	Fenit	T. Brosnan
Cloghane (Rathmore DDC)	Castlegregory	Dingle	--	T. de Lacy
Clohane (Rathmore DDC)	Killarney	Headford 5	--	B. O'Riordan
Coolacarrig (Listowel DDC)	Listowel	Listowel 4	'Coolacarrig Creamery, Listowel'	C. Clancy
Cordal (Dicksgrove DDC)	Castleisland	Castleisland	--	W. Maloney
Dromcough (Lixnaw CDS)	Listowel	Listowel 5	Listowel	J. O'Connor
Duagh (Listowel DDC)	Duagh, Kilmorna	Kilmorna 5	'Duagh Creamery, Kilmorna	T. Costelloe
Feonagh (Dingle DDC)	Dingle	Dingle	'Feonagh, Dingle'	D. Healy

LIST OF AUXILIARY CREAMERIES IN IRELAND (Continued)

Name of Creamery & Owners	Post Town	Miles to Nearest Railway Station	Telephone No Telegraphic Address	Name of Manager
Firies (Castlemaine DDC)	Farranfore	Molahiffe	'Firies Cry.,Farranfore'	M. Egan
Glenderry (Ballinclemessig)	Ballyheigue, Tralee	Ardfert 10	'Co-operative, Ballyheigue'	John Dineen
Glenbeigh (Castlemaine DDC)	Glenbeigh	Glenbeigh 1	Glenbeigh	James Barry
Gortatlea (Dicksgrove DDC)	Gortatlea, Tralee	Gortatlea	'Gortatlea, Ballymacelligott'	J. McEllistrim
Gullane (Rathmore DDC)	Rathmore	Rathmore 3	Rathmore	T. Kelliher
Kielduff (Lee Strand CDS)	Rathanny, Tralee	Tralee 5	Ballymacelligott	M. Enright
Kilcoleman (Listowel DDC)	Astee, Ballylongford	Listowel 10	'Kilcoleman Cry, Astee'	P. Dowling
Kilcummin (Dicksgrove DDC)	Killarney	Killarney 6	Killarney	M. Freil
Killorglin (Castlemaine DDC	Killorglin	Killorglin	'Creamery ,Killorglin'	J. P. Burke
Kilflynn (Abbeydorney)	Kilflynn	Abbeydorney 3	'Creamery Kilflynn'	P. Lawlor
Kilmorna (Listowel DDC)	Kilmorna ,Duagh	Kilmorna	'Creamery, Kilmorna' Tel. Listowel 80	M. Lynch
Lisselton (Listowel DDC)	Lisselton	Listowel 6	Lisselton	J. G. Hanrahan
Lispole (Dingle DDC)	Dingle	Dingle 6	Dingle	E. O'Connor
Listry (Castlemaine DDC)	Listry, Miltown	Miltown 3	'Listry, Creamery, Miltown'	C. Ferris
Lyrecrompane (Listowel DDC)	Listowel	Listowel 10	Listowel	J. O'Sullivan
Scortlea (Lixnaw CDS)	Listowel	Listowel 3	Listowel	J. B. Lovett
Stradbally (Dingle DDC)	Stradbally, Castlegregory	Castlegregory 2	Castlegregory	M. Griffin
Scartaglen (Dicksgrove DDC)	Farranfore	Castleisland 6	Castleisland	Pk. Egan
Tarbert (Listowel DDC)	Tarbert	Foynes 10	'Creamery , Tarbert, Kerry'	J. A. Ruddle
Tobermaing (Dicksgrove DDC)	Castleisland	Castleisland 1	Castleisland	D. Houlihan
Valentia (Caherciveen DDC)	Valencia	Valencia	'Creamery, Valencia'	J. Murphy
Ventry (Dingle DDC)	Dingle	Dingle	'Ventry Creamery, Dingle	J. Looney

LIST OF AUXILIARY CREAMERIES IN IRELAND (Continued)

Name of Creamery & Owners	Post Town	Miles to Nearest Railway Station	Telephone No Telegraphic Address	Name of Manager
Co. Kilkenny				
Ballyfrunk (Kilmanagh CDS)	Callen	Kilkenny 5	Kilmanagh	F. McClusky
Ballybur (Kilkenny)	Cuffe's Grange	Kilkenny 5	'Creamery Ballybur'	B. Twomey
Ballyfoyle (Muckalee CDS)	Ballyfoyle	Kilkenny 4	Jenkins town	E. Byrne
Brandon Vale CDS (Indept.-Barrow vale CC)	Greig-na-managh	Borris 5	'Creamery Greig-na-managh'	J. Ryan
Castlewarren (Muckalee CDS)	Castlewarren	Gowran 6	Gowran	P. Dolan
Clogga (Piltown)	Mooncoin	Grange 1	Mooncoin, Co. Kilkenny	J. Sheehan
Coon (Muckalee CDS)	Muine Bheag	Castlecomer 6	Coon, Castlecomer	J. Hahessy
Grange (Fennor CDS)	Urlingford	Laffan's Bridge 11	Gurtnahoe	P. Holohan
Harristown (Mullinavat CDS)	Piltown	Mullinavat 4	Mullinavat	J. Reid
Knockmoylan (Mullinavat CDS)	Knockmoylan ,Mullinavat	Mullinavat 5	'Creamery, Knockmoylan, Mullinavat'	J. Holden
Loughcullen (Glenmore CDS)	Kilmacow, near Waterford	Kilmacow 2	'Cry ,Loughcullen Kilmacow' Tel Kilmacow 7116	W. Cahill
Mullinbeg (Piltown)	Piltown	Fiddown 4	Piltown	M. Cahill
Mountgeale (Kilkenny CDS)	Tullaroan	Kilkenny 7	'Mountgeale Cry, Tullaroan'	T. Murphy
Sleiverue CC (Glenmore)	Sleiverue near Waterford	Waterford 3	'Creamery, Sleiverue' Tel. Waterford 4436	R. Mahony
Woodstock (Nore Valley CDS)	Clodiagh, Inistioge	New Ross 7	'Creamery Inistioge'	M.J. Murray
Co. Leitrim				
Aughavas (Kiltoghert CDS)	Carrigallen	Mohill 7	'Cry, Aughavas, Carrigallen'	J. Cullen
Bornacoola (Kiltoghert CDS)	Johnson's Bridge Dromond	Dronond 6	'Creamery Johnson's Bridge ,Dromond'	E. Kelly
Breffni (Indept.- Drumcliffe CDS)	Dromahair	Dromahair	'Creamery, Dromahair'	E. Clinton
Creevelea (Killasnett)	Drumkeeran	Dromahair 7	'Cry, Creevelea, Drumkeeran'	J. Mc Gurrin
Dowra CDS (Indept.- Killasnet)	Dowra	Glenfarne 10	Glenfarne	M. Rooney

201

LIST OF AUXILIARY CREAMERIES IN IRELAND (Continued)

Name of Creamery & Owners	Post Town	Miles to Nearest Railway Station	Telephone No Telegraphic Address	Name of Manager
Co. Kilkenny				
Ballyfrunk (Kilmanagh CDS)	Callen	Kilkenny 5	Kilmanagh	F. McClusky
Ballybur (Kilkenny)	Cuffe's Grange	Kilkenny 5	'Creamery Ballybur'	B. Twomey
Ballyfoyle (Muckalee CDS)	Ballyfoyle	Kilkenny 4	Jenkins town	E. Byrne
Brandon Vale CDS (Indept.-Barrow vale CC)	Greig-na-managh	Borris 5	'Creamery Greig-na-managh'	J. Ryan
Castlewarren (Muckalee CDS)	Castlewarren	Gowran 6	Gowran	P. Dolan
Clogga (Piltown)	Mooncoin	Grange 1	Mooncoin, Co. Kilkenny	J. Sheehan
Coon (Muckalee CDS)	Muine Bheag	Castlecomer 6	Coon, Castlecomer	J. Hahessy
Grange (Fennor CDS)	Urlingford	Laffan's Bridge 11	Gurtnahoe	P. Holohan
Harristown (Mullinavat CDS)	Piltown	Mullinavat 4	Mullinavat	J. Reid
Knockmoylan (Mullinavat CDS)	Knockmoylan ,Mullinavat	Mullinavat 5	'Creamery, Knockmoylan, Mullinavat'	J. Holden
Loughcullen (Glenmore CDS)	Kilmacow, near Waterford	Kilmacow 2	'Cry ,Loughcullen Kilmacow' Tel Kilmacow 7116	W. Cahill
Mullinbeg (Piltown)	Piltown	Fiddown 4	Piltown	M. Cahill
Mountgeale (Kilkenny CDS)	Tullaroan	Kilkenny 7	'Mountgeale Cry, Tullaroan'	T. Murphy
Sleiverue CC (Glenmore)	Sleiverue near Waterford	Waterford 3	'Creamery, Sleiverue' Tel. Waterford 4436	R. Mahony
Woodstock (Nore Valley CDS)	Clodiagh, Inistioge	New Ross 7	'Creamery Inistioge'	M.J. Murray
Co. Leitrim				
Aughavas (Kiltoghert CDS)	Carrigallen	Mohill 7	'Cry, Aughavas, Carrigallen'	J. Cullen
Bornacoola (Kiltoghert CDS)	Johnson's Bridge Dromond	Dronond 6	'Creamery Johnson's Bridge ,Dromond'	E. Kelly
Breffni (Indept.- Drumcliffe CDS)	Dromahair	Dromahair	'Creamery, Dromahair'	E. Clinton
Creevelea (Killasnett)	Drumkeeran	Dromahair 7	'Cry, Creevelea, Drumkeeran'	J. Mc Gurrin
Dowra CDS (Indept.- Killasnet)	Dowra	Glenfarne 10	Glenfarne	M. Rooney

LIST OF AUXILIARY CREAMERIES IN IRELAND (Continued)

Name of Creamery & Owners	Post Town	Miles to Nearest Railway Station	Telephone No Telegraphic Address	Name of Manager
Ballylanders (Knocklong CMC)	Ballylanders	Knocklong	Ballylanders	**Daniel Hayes**
Ballyorgan (Effin CDS)	Kilfinane	Kilmallock 6	Kilfinane	**J. F. McCarthy**
Ballinena (Ardagh)	Newcastlewest	Newcastlewest 3	Newcastlewest	**M. O'Connell**
Banogue (Bruree CDS)	Croom	Croom 4	'Banogue Creamery, Croom'	**J.J. Murphy**
Breakayle CC (Oola CDS)	Pallasgreen	Pallasgreen 2	Pallasgreen	**J. Kennedy**
Broadford (Kantogher)	Broadford, Charleville	Newcastlewest 3	'Creamery, Broadford, Co. Limerick.' Tel. Broadford 2	**John Quinlivan**
Bulgaden (Knocklong CMC)	Bulgaden, Kilmallock	Kilmallock 2	'Bulgaden, Creamery, Kilmallock'	**M. English**
Carnahalla (Tipperary CC)	Doon	Oola 6	Doon	**M. Lacey**
Castle Conyers (Ballyagran CDS)	Charleville	Charleville 7	Ballyagran	**J. P. McElligott**
Colemanswell(Ballyagran CDS)	Foxhall, Charleville	Charleville 4	'Foxhall Cry, Charleville'	**D. O'Connell**
Coerlish Creamery (Dromkeen CMC Condensery)	Pallasgreen	Dromkeen	'Dromkeen Auxiliary Cry,.'	**J. O'Riordan**
Cratloe (Athea CC)	Cratloe, Abbeyfeale	Abbeyfeale 2	'Cry, Cratloe, Abbeyfeale'	**E. C. Leahy**
Darragh (Mitchelstown CDS)	Kilfinane	Kilmallock 8	Kilfinane	**C. O'Keeffe**
Dromkeen CM Condensery	Pallasgreen	Dromkeen 2	Tel. Dromkeen 3	**T. Hegarty**
Dromin (Kilmallock CDS)	Shearin's Cross, Kilmallock	Kilmallock 4	'Ballinstona, Bruff'	**S. O'Connor**
Drumcollogher (Milford)	Charleville	Charleville 10	'Creamery, Dromcollogher'	**P. Noonan**
Elton (Knocklong CMC)	Knocklong	Knocklong 6	'Elton Cry, Knocklong'	**M. Coffey**
Fedamore Co-op Creamery (Drombanna CDS)	Grange, Kilmallock	Croom 7	'Grange, Kilmallock'	**F. J. Barry**
Galbally (Kilross CDS)	Galbally	Emly 5	Galbally	**Patk. Danagher**
Garryduff (Kantogher CDS)	Newcastlewest	Newcastlewest 3	'Cry, Garryduff, Strand' Tel. Newcastlewest, 37	**Timothy Geary**
Glosha (Cappamore CDS)	Cappamore	Dromkeen 5	'Cry, Glosha, Cappamore'	**M. Gleeson**
Gormanstown (Knocklong)	Knocklong	Knocklong 5	'Cleeve, Gormanstown'	**M. Murphy**
Glounlahan (Mount Collins CDS)	Brosna, Abbeyfeale.	Abbeyfeale 10	Brosna	**J. Leahy**

LIST OF AUXILIARY CREAMERIES IN IRELAND (Continued)

Name of Creamery & Owners	Post Town	Miles to Nearest Railway Station	Telephone No Telegraphic Address	Name of Manager
Headley's Bridge (Feale Bridge CDS)	Abbeyfeale	Abbeyfeale 6	Abbeyfeale	N. Cotter
Kilfinane (Kilmallock CDS)	Kilfinane	Kilmallock 5	'Kilfinane'	Wm. Keane
Killonan (Drombanna CC)	Killonan, Caherconlish	Killonan	'Killonan Creamery, Caherconlish'	P. J. O'Connell
Knockadea (Mitchelstown)	Ballylanders	Mitchelstown 6	Ballylanders	J. Burke
Knockcarron (Knocklong CMC)	Knocklong	Knocklong 3	'Cleeve's Knockcarron, Knocklong'	J. O'Riordan
Knockaney (Knocklong CMC)	Hospital	Knocklong 4	'Cleeve's Knockaney, Bruff'	T. Egan
Lisnalty (Drombanna CDS)	Limerick	Limerick 3	Limerick	J. Riordan
Mannister (Grey bridge CDS)	Mannister, Croom	Croom 2	'Clineeve, Mannister, Croom'	M. Sheahan
Meenahela Bridge (Tournafulla CDS)	Abbeyfeale	Devon Road 2	'Meenahela Cry, Tournafulla'	W. P. Curtin
Milltown (Knocklong CMC)	Croagh, Rathkeale	Rathkeale 4	Croagh	T. Magner
Monagea (Castlemahon CDS)	Newcastlewest	Patrickswell 1	'Cream Dairy, Monagea Strand'	J. Galvin
Patrickswell (Black Abbey)	Limerick	Pallas 1	Patrickswell	J. O'Farrell
Race (Sarsfield CDS)	Race, Pallasgreen	Newmarket 12	'Creamery, race, Pallasgreen'	M. Bourke
Rockchapel (Mount Collins CDS)	Abbeyfeale	Pallas 2	Rockchapel	D. E. O'Connell
Reenavana (Toher CDS)	Doon	--	--	P. Cunningham
Tullybrackey (Glin CDS)	Bruff	Ardagh 8	Bruff	L. Hogan
Turraree (Glin CDS)	Turraree , Athea	Foynes 9	'Turraree Co-op., Glin'	P. Mullane PC
Co. Longford				
Ballinadee (Killeshandra CA &DS)	Ballinadee	Edgeworthstown 6	Ballinadee	B. O'Reilly
Longford (Killeshandra)	Longford			J. O'Connor
Co. Meath Oldcastle (Indept. Annagelliffe CDS)	Cloghan Strand, Oldcastle	Oldcastle	Oldcastle	F. Reilly

LIST OF AUXILIARY CREAMERIES IN IRELAND (Continued)

Name of Creamery & Owners	Post Town	Miles to Nearest Railway Station	Telephone No Telegraphic Address	Name of Manager
Co. Monaghan				
Averleagh (Lough Egish CDS)	Clontibrit PO	Monaghan 3	Clontibrit	**J. Duffy**
Ballinode CA & DS (Indept-Town of Monaghan)	Monaghan	Castleblaney 3	Ballinode	**A. Montgomery**
Carrickaslane (Lough Egish CDS)	Castleblaney	Newbliss 3	'Creamery, Carrickaslane, Castleblaney'	**Jas. F. Campbell**
Cloverhill (Clones)	Drum, Clones	Monaghan Road 2	Newbliss	**A. Mills**
Corcaghan CDS (Indept.-Town of Monaghan)	Stranooden	Newbliss 3	'Creamery Corcaghan, Monaghan'	**G. McCormack**
Doapey CDS (Indept.-Clones CDS)	Doapey, Newbliss	Doonhamlet	'Doapey Cry., Newbliss	**M. Tobin**
Doohamlet (Lough Egish CDS)	Doohamlet, Castleblaney	Monaghan 4	'Creamery Doohamlet'	**Vacant**
Drumacruttin (Lough Egish CDS)	Stranoden	Newcastle	'Drunacruttin Creamery, Monaghan'	**P. McNally**
Magheracloone (Lough Egish CDS)	Carrigmacross	Carrigmacross 4	--	**Owen McNally**
Mullaghhanee (Lough Egish CDS)	Castleblaney	Castleblaney 3	Castleblaney	**B. Coleman**
Newbliss CDS (Clones CDS)	Newbliss	Newbliss	'Creamery Newbliss	**J. Murphy**
Rawdeerpark (Clones CDS)	Newbliss	Clones 2	Newbliss	**Vacant**
Scotch Corner (Lough Egish CDS)	Ballybay PO	Ballybay 3	Ballybay	**E. Connolly**
Scotshouse (Clones CDS)	Clones	Clones 5	Clones	**P. Hand**
Smithboro' (Town of Monaghan CDS)	Smithboro'	Smithboro'	'Creamery Smithboro'	**P. Hanley**
Tattybrack (Lough Egish CDS)	Rockcoeey	Rockcorry 2	'Creamery Rockcorry'	**P. Coyle**
Tyholland (Town of Monaghan CDS)	Silverstream	Glasslough 3	'Creamery Mittletown'	**P. Cahill**

LIST OF AUXILIARY CREAMERIES IN IRELAND (Continued)

Name of Creamery & Owners	Post Town	Miles to Nearest Railway Station	Telephone No Telegraphic Address	Name of Manager
Co. Roscommon				
Ballaghadereen CDS (Indept.- Gurteen CDS)	Ballaghadereen	Ballaghadereen	'Creamery Ballaghdereen'	J. Bambrick
Croghan (Kiltoghert)	Croghan, Boyle	Boyle 6	'Creamery Croghan'	J. Pettit
Knockvicar (Kiltoghert CA & DS)	Knockvicar			
Seefin (Riverstown CDS)	Seefin, Clonlough, Boyle	Kilfree Junct. 3	'Seefin Creamery Gurteen, Sligo'	Patk. Gallagher
Co. Sligo				
Aclare (Rathscanlon CDS	Aclare	Tubbercurry 7	'Creamery Aclare'	Closed
Ballintogher (Riverstown)	Ballintogher	Ballintogher 1	'Creamery Ballintogher'	P. Morrow
Ballymote (Riverstown CDS)	Ballymote	Ballymote	'Creamery Ballymote'	Mrs J. McNulty
Bunninadden (Achonery CDS)	Ballymote	Ballymote 4	Bunninadden	J. Anderson
Calry (Drumcliffe CDS)	\Calry	Sligo 5	--	P. J. Waters
Clohogue (Riverstown CDS)	Castlebaldwin, Boyle	Ballymote 6	'Creamery, Castlebaldwin, Ballinafad '	F. Keirns
Collooney (Drumcliffe)	Collooney	Collooney	'Creamery Collooney '	Thomas Smith
Cloonacool (Achonry)	Tubbercurry	Tubbercurry 3	'Creamery Cloonacool Tubbercurry'	Thos. O'Grady
Coolaney (Achonry)	Coolaney	Leyney 1	Coolaney	C. Wims
Geevagh CDS (Indept.- Riverstown CDS)	Boyle	Collooney 14	Ballyfaron	T. Phelan
Keash (Riverstown CDS)	Ballymote	Ballymote 5	'Creamery Keash, Ballymote'	D. McManamy
Skreen (Achonry)	Skreen	Ballisodare 9	'Creamery Skreen'	J. Clerkin
Co. Tipperary				
Alleen (Tipperary CC)	Dundrum	Dundrum 3	'Alleen Cry, Dundrum'	T. Baragry
Annacarty (Tipperary CMC)	Annacarty, Tipperary	Dundrum 3	'Cry, Annacarty, Cappawhite'	J. Hanly
Ardfinnan (Suirvale)	Cahir	Cahir 6	Ardfinnan	John Holmes

LIST OF AUXILIARY CREAMERIES IN IRELAND (Continued)

Name of Creamery & Owners	Post Town	Miles to Nearest Railway Station	Telephone No Telegraphic Address	Name of Manager
Co. Tipperary – Cond.				
Ballinard (Tipperary CDS)	Schronell, Tipp	Limerick Junction 4	'Cry, Ballinard, Lattin'	**P. J. McCormack**
Ballinure (Knockavardagh)	Thurles	Laffan's Bridge 3	'Killenaule	**Denis Ryan**
Ballinurra (Piltown)	Carrick-on-Suir	Carrick-on-Suir 3	'Creamery Ballinurra'	**J Crean**
Ballybrack (Tipp. CMC)	Annacarty	Dundrum 4	'Ballybrack, Annacarty'	**W. F. Cusack**
Ballydough (Hollyford)	Milestone, Thurles	Dundrum 14	Hollyford	**James Quirke**
Ballygriffin (Tipperary CC)	Golden, Cashel	Dundrum 3	'Cry, Ballygriffin Golden'	**P. O'Dwyer**
Ballylooby (Suirvale)	Cahir	Cahir 5	Cahir	**M. McCarthy**
Ballyporeen (Mitchelstown CC)	Ballyporeen, Cahir	Mitchelstown 9	'Creamery, Ballyporeen'	**F. J. Cotter**
Ballyduag (Centenary CDS)	Ballyduag, Thurles	Thurles 5	'Creamery Ballyduag, Thurles'	**Jas. Leahy**
Ballysloe (Fennor CDS)	New Birmingham, Thurles	Laffansbridge 7	'Ballysloe Dairy, Gurtnahoe'	**P. J. Fitzgerald**
Ballyvistea (Sarsfield CDS)	Emly, Knocklong	Emly 3	'Cry, Ballyvistea, Emly'	**J. O'Donovan**
Bansha (Tipp. CMC)	Bansha	Bansha	'Creamery Bansha'	**T. Keane**
Birdhill Co-op Creamery Ltd (Indept.- Annacotty)	Birdhill nr Limerick	Birdhill	Co-op Creamery, Birdhill'	**J. Anketel**
Blackbridge (Tipp. CMC)	Dundrum, Cashel	Dundrum	Dundrum	**John Quirke**
Carrick-on-Suir (Millvale)	Carrick-on-Suir	Carrick-on-Suir	Carrick-on-Suir	**D. McCarthy**
Cashel (Centenary CDS)	Cashel	Cashel	'Dairy Cashel, Tipperary'	**J. Stapleton**
Clerihan (Indept)	Clerihan	Clonmel 5	Clerihan	**J. Cooney**
Clodia CDS (Indept.- Borrisoleigh	Greenane, Borrisoleigh	Thurles	Borrisoleigh PO	**Jas. Kennedy**

LIST OF AUXILIARY CREAMERIES IN IRELAND (Continued)

Name of Creamery & Owners	Post Town	Miles to Nearest Railway Station	Telephone No Telegraphic Address	Name of Manager
Clogheen (Suirvale)	Clogheen, Cahir	Cahir	'Creamery Clogheen'	M. Collins
Clonbrick (Solohead)	Ayle, Oola	Oola	Oola	M. Cosgrave
Cloncannon CDS (Indept.- Borrisoleigh)	Moneygall, Cloughjordan	Cloughjordan	'Creamery, Cloncannon, Moneygall	J. Gray
Clogher (Tipp CMC)	Gooldscross	Gooldscross 4	'Clogher,Goldscross'	M. Gleeson
Cloran (Coolmoyne & Fethard CDS)	Cloneen, Fethard	Fethard 3	Fethard	P. Murphy
Commonaline (Hollyford)	Doon	Oola 8	Doon	Vacant
Croughmorka (Upperchurch CDS)	Croughmorka, Doon	Pallas 10	'Creamery, Croughmorka, Doon'	J. Carey
Currabaha (Borrisoleigh CDS)	Borrisoleigh	Templemore 9	Templederry	T. Ryan
Donohill (Tipperary CC)	Tipperary	Dundrum 4	'Co-op , Cry., Donohill'	D. Hanley
Duharra Co-op Cry.(Nenagh CC)	Newtown, Nenagh	Nenagh 5	Cry. Newtown, Nenagh'	C Greally
Dungrud (Tipperary CDS)	Galbally	Galbally 3	'Dungrud, Creamery Galbally '	J. Hayes
Fethard (Coolmoyne &Fethard Creamery)	Fethard	Fethard	Tel. Fethard 16	R. Hogan
Glenough (Tipp. CMC)	Gooldscross	Gooldscross 7	Rossmore	J. Kildunne
Golden Co-op Creamery (Outhrath CDS)	Cashel	Cashel 4	'Creamery, Golden, Cashel'	John Heffernan
Grange (Tipp. CMC)	Cashel	Cashel 6	Cashel	A. O'Hare
Grantstown (Tipp CMC)	Grantstown, Tipperary	Dundrum 6	'Grantstown Cry, Tipperary'	M. O'Sullivan
Greenane (Tipp.CMC)	Tipperary	Tipperary 3	'Cry., Greenane, Tipperary'	P. Boucher-Hayes
Gurtagarry Co-op Creamery Ltd. (Indept.-Borrisoleigh)	Toomevara, Nenagh	Nenagh 11	'Creamery, Gurtagarry, Toomevara'	Daniel Lonergan
Holycross (Thurles CDS)	Holycross	Thurles 4	'Creamery, Holycross'	M. J. Ryan
Kilcommon (Holyford CDS	Thurles	Pallas 12	'Creamery, Kilcommon'	J. McGrath
Killea CDS (Indept.-Centenary)	Killea, Templemore	Templemore 3	'Cry., Killea, Templemore	T. Shanahan

LIST OF AUXILIARY CREAMERIES IN IRELAND (Continued)

Name of Creamery & Owners	Post Town	Miles to Nearest Railway Station	Telephone No Telegraphic Address	Name of Manager
Killeen CDS (Nenagh CC)	Killeen, Nenagh	Nenagh	'Killeen Cry., Templederry'	J. Gleeson
Killerk (Coolmoyne & Fethard)	Killerk, Fethard	Fethard 3	'Killerk Cry., Fethard' Tel. Fethard 34	T. Tierney
Kilmoyler (Tipp. CMC)	Kilmoyler ,Cahir	Bansha 3	Bansha	J. Lonergan
Kiloscully (Indept.- Newport)	Newport	Castleconnell 10	Newport	W. Bourke
Kilvilcarris CDS Ltd. (Indept.- Borrisoleigh)	Drom, Thurles	Templemore 4	'Drom Cry., Templemore'	L. Egan
Knockline CDS (Indept.- Newport)	Newport	Nenagh 12	'Knockline Cry., Newport'	M. O'Doherty
Knockulty (Callen CDS)	Mullinahone	Kilkenny 14	'Creamery, Knockulty'	R. Grace
Kyle (Kilmanagh CDS)	The Commons, Thurles	Laffansbridge 12	'Ballingarry, Thurles'	Thomas Walsh
Lagganstown (Outrath CDS)	Golden, Cashel	Bansha 6	Golden	O. Cleary
Littleton (Centenary CDS)	Littleton	Horse and Jockey 2	Littleton	P. English
Loran (Centenary CDS)	Shanakill, Curraguneen, Roscrea	Lisduff 3	Curraguneen	W. J. Buckley
Loughmore (Centenary CDS)	Loughmore	Templemore 4	Templemore	W. Delaney
Montore (Centenary)	Clonakenny, Roscrea	Templemore 7	'Montore Creamery, Clonakenny'	J. Durack
Pallas (Indept.-Drombane CDS)	Borrisoleigh	Thurles 9	'Pallas Cry Borrisoleigh'	W. Ryan
Rear Cross CDS (Indept- Upperchurch)	Newport	Pallas 9	'Cry., Rear Cross, Kilcommon'	T. Downes
Reiska (Upperchurch CA & DS)	Kilcommon, Thurles	Thurles 15	'Cry., Reiska, Kilcommon'	J. Caplis
Rossadrehid (Tipperary CDS)	Bansha	Bansha 2	'Aherlow Creamery, Bansha'	John Cusack
Rossmore (Tipperary CMC)	Gouldscross	Gouldscross 3	'Society, Rossmore'	Rd. Maher
Silvermines CDS Ltd (Indept.- Nenagh)	Silvermines, Nenagh	Nenagh 5	'Creamery, Silvermines'	M. J. Minihan

LIST OF AUXILIARY CREAMERIES IN IRELAND (Continued)

Name of Creamery & Owners	Post Town	Miles to Nearest Railway Station	Telephone No Telegraphic Address	Name of Manager
St. Ailbes (Tipperary Co-op Creamery Ltd.)	Emly, Knocklong	Emly	'St. Ailbes cry. Emly'	D. O'Mahony
Springmount CA & DS Ltd. (Indept)	Clonmel	Clonmel 5	'Creamery, Springmount, Clerihan'	J. J. Keane BSc
Templederry (Borrisoleigh)	Thurles	Nenagh 9	'Creamery Templederry	J. Doherty
Templetouhy CC Ltd. (Indept.- Centenary)	Templemore	Templemore 4	'Templemore	W. Fogarty
Templeree Castleiney CDS (Indept.- Centenary)	Templemore	Templemore 3	'Creamery, Castleiney, Templemore'	W. Davy
Toomevara (Nenagh CDS)	Toomevara, Nenagh	Nenagh 6	'Creamery, Toomevara'	Martin Minihan
Turraheen (Dromane CDS)	Rossmore	Gooldscross 4	Rossmore	D. B. English

Co. Waterford

Name of Creamery & Owners	Post Town	Miles to Nearest Railway Station	Telephone No Telegraphic Address	Name of Manager
Aglish (Dungarvan CC)	Aglish	Cappoquin 5	Aglish	D. McGrath
Ballyduff (Castlelyons CDS)	Ballyduff	Ballyduff	'Creamery Ballyduff'	J. Finn
Ballydurn (Kilmeadan CC)	Clonea, Carrick-on-Suir	Kilmacthomas 5	'Creamery ,Ballydurn, Kilmacthomas'	Ml. A. Phelan
Blackwater Valley (Knockmeal CC)	Cappoquin	Cappoquin	'Creamery Cappoquin' Tel. Cappoquin 16	C. Enright
Cappagh (Dungarvan CC)	Cappagh	Cappagh	Cappoquin	M. Phelan
Carroll's Cross (Kilmeadan CC)	Carroll's Cross, Kilmacthoms	Carroll's Cross	'Creamery, Carroll's Cross, Kilmacthomas'	R. Walsh
Clashmore (Dungarvan CC)	Clashmore	Youghal 8	'Creamery, Clashmore'	J. Cass
Cullen Castle (Kilmeadan)	Tramore	Tramore 2	Tramore	P. Daly BSc.
Durrow (Dungarvan CC)	Durrow, Stradbally	Durrow	'Creamery, Stradbally'	R. Lucey
Grange (Dungarvan CC)	Grange, Youghal	Youghal 8	'Cry., Grange, Youghal'	Jas. Prendergast

LIST OF AUXILIARY CREAMERIES IN IRELAND (Continued)

Name of Creamery & Owners	Post Town	Miles to Nearest Railway Station	Telephone No Telegraphic Address	Name of Manager
Co. Waterford (Continued)				
Kill (Kilmeaden CC)	Kill, Kilmacthomas	Carrolls Cross 6	'Creamery, Kill, Co. Waterford'	M. J. Kennedy
Mahon Bridge (Dungarvan CDS)	Kilmacthomas	Kilmacthomas 4	' Creamery, Mahon Bridge, Kilmacthomas'	D. Begley
Mothel (MillvaleCDS)	Mothel, Clonea	Carrick-on-Suir	'Cry., Mothel, Carrick-on-Suir'	J. Nolan
Newcastle (Clonmel & Newcastle	Ballymacarbery	Clonmel 8	Newcastle	C. Fleming
Nire Valley (Knockmeal CDS)	Ballymacarbery	Clonmel 10	'Co-operative Cry, Ballymacarbery' Tel. Ballymacarbery 3	M. J. Desmond
Old Parish (Dungarvan CC)	Ballinacart, Dungarvan	Dunvarvan 9	'Creamery, Old Parish, Dungarvan'	Luke Brennan PC
Rathgormack (Millvale CDS)	Rathgarmack, Carrick-on-Suir	Carrick-on-Suir 6	'Creamery, Rathgormack, Carrick-on-Suir'	J. A. O'Shea
Scartbridge (Knockmeal CDS)	Ballinamult, Clonmel	Cappagh 8	'Creamery, Scartbridge,Ballinamult'	P. Desmond
Tallow (Castlelyons CDS)	Tallow	Tallow Road 4	'Creamery, Tallow'	E. Morrissey
Co. Wexford				
Kilmuckridge (Inch CDS)	Ballycanew	Ferns 8	Ballycanew	Vacant
Macamore (Inch CDS)	Ballycanew, Gorey	Gorey 5	'Creamery Ballycanew, Tel. Ballycanew 2	J. Malone

211

LIST OF CENTRES IN NORTHERN IRELAND LICENCED TO PASTURISE AND PROCESS MILK RECEIVED FROM PRODUCERS

C   **denotes Central Creamery**   **F denotes Milk Factory**

AC   **denotes Auxiliary Creamery**   **D denotes milk Distributer**

Name of Creamery & Owners	Post Town	Miles to Nearest Railway Station	Telephone No Telegraphic Address	Name of Manager
County Antrim				
Ballynure Milk Depot C (Milk Marketing Board for NI (MMBNI)	Ballynure	Ballyclare	Ballyclare 212	**R. W. Hyde**
Ulster Creameries AC and D (Ballyarney) (MMBNI)	Ballyarney	Whitehead	Whitehead 274	**T. Emerson**
Dromona Milk Depot F (Ministry of Agr. NI)	Cullybacky	Cullybacky	Cullybacky 253	**A. McAfee**
Nestle's Milk Products Ltd. F	Ballymoney	Ballymoney	Ballymoney 137	**C. L. Cooper**
Rathkenny CA & DS	Rathkenny	Ballymena	Martinstown —	**W. P. Hamilton**
Johnston's Dairy D	Ballymena	Ballymena	Ballymena 6246	**A. N. Johnston**
Deerpark CA & DS, AC	Glenarm	Larne	Glenarm 227	**J. Baxter**
Boyd's Dairy, D	Finaghy	Finaghy	Belfast 67862	**J. Boyd**
Armagh				
Messrs. Bovril Ltd F	Magheralin	Moira	Moira 274	**R. S. McVeigh**
CWS Ltd F	Tu;;ygoonigan. Armagh	Armagh	Armagh 414	**G. W. Snelgrove**
Creamline Products Ltd AC and D	Lurgan	Lurgan	Lurgan 385	**J. W. Mcormak**
Fane Valley CA & DS D	Armagh	Armagh	Armagh 294	**A. Smith**
Tassagh milk Depot MMBNI F	Tassagh	Tassagh	Keady 237	**W. J. Orr**
County Down				
Armaghdown Creameries Ltd. C & D	Newry	Newry	Newry 320	**J. Getty**
Bangor Wholesale Dairies Ltd. D	Bangor	Bangor	Bangor 1871	**R. Quinn**

LIST OF CENTRES IN NORTHERN IRELAND LICENCED TO PASTURISE AND PROCESS MILK RECEIVED FROM PRODUCERS

C   denotes **Central Creamery**   **F**   denotes **Milk Factory**

AC   denotes **Auxiliary Creamery**   **D**   denotes **milk Distributer**

Name of Creamery & Owners	Post Town	Miles to Nearest Railway Station	Telephone No Telegraphic Address	Name of Manager
Belfast Co. Borough				
Belfast Co-op. Soc. Ltd. C and D	Belfast	Belfast	Belfast 59451	W. T. Thompson
Bamford's Dairy D	Belfast	Belfast	Belfast 67639	R. W. Bamford
Dobsons Dairy Ltd. C and D	Belfast	Belfast	Belfast 42901	C. Damoglou
Kennedy Bros. D	Belfast	Belfast	Belfast 27717	T. Kennedy
Ulster Creameries D	Belfast	Belfast	Belfast 57258	A. M. Butler
Cregagh Dairy Ltd C	Belfast	Belfast	Belfast 57941	R. Gibony
Derry				
Fisons Food Products F	Coleraine	Coleraine	Coleraine 541	R. C. Anderson
Ballyrashane CA & DS C and D	Cloyfin	Coleraine	Coleraine 54	R. A. Irwin
J Deery & Sons D	Derry	Derry	Derry 3555	J. Deery
Leckpatrick Co-op D	Derry	Derry	Derry 3221	W. J. Simpson
Nestlé's Food Products F	Castledawson	Castledawson	Castledawson 541	T. E. S. Hayter
Co Fermanagh				
Derrygonnelly Co-op C and D	Derrygonnelly	\Enniskillen	Derrygonnelly 203	S. Fawcett
Erne CA&DS C and D	Kesh	Kesh	Kesh 303	S. Gibson
Irvinestown CA&DS C and D	Irvinestown	Irvinestown	Irvinestown 219	A, N. Crawford
S.C.W.S Ltd. C and D	Enniskillen	Enniskillen	Enniskillen 2058	R. Magee
Springfield CA&DS	Springfield	Enniskillen	Springfield 202	R. McCullough
Lisnaskea Milk Depot MMBNI F	Lisnaskea	Lisnaskea	Lisnaskea 262	W. Scott
Co. Tyrone				
Augher CA&DS AC	Augher	Sixmilecross	Clogher 214	P. W. Trotter
Dunman Bridge Milk Depot MMBNI	Cookstown	Cookstown	Cookstown 330	W. J. Steele
Fivemiletown CA&DS C and D	Fivemiletown	Maguires Bridge	Fivemiletown 209	J. Haire
Killen CA&DS AC	Castlederg	Victoria Br.	Castlederg 215	W. J. Patterson
Killyman MD, MMBNI	Moy	Threw & Moy	Moy 270	W. Wilson
Killyman CS&DS D	Moy	Threw & Moy	Strabane 275	R. Wallace
Leckpatrick CA&DS C & D	Artigarvan, Strabane	Strabane		
Nestle's Food. Products F	Omagh	Omagh	Omagh 245	J. A. Simmons
Nestle's Food. Products F	Victoria Bridge	Victoria Bridge	Sion Mills 220	G. P. Pinder

LIST OF
ASSISTANT MANAGERS IN IRELAND

CAVAN

Annagelliffe CDS Ltd	R.MORROW
Baileboro CDS Ltd	J. COONEY
Killeshandra CDS Ltd	J. SMYTH
	P. SEXTON
Kilnaleck CA & DS Ltd	P. J. Mc ADAMS

CLARE

East Clare Creameries Ltd	D. B. O'HANLON
	P. O'DWYER
Travelling Creameries	M. O'HALLORAN
	J. NAGLE
	D. SCANLON
	E. CRONIN
North Clare Creameries Ltd	D. J. O'DWYER BSc
	VINCENT BARRETT
Junior	J. KELLEHER
Travelling Creameries	E. COTTER
	P. CLANCY
	M. WHELTON, BSc
	J. CRONIN
	C. O'SHEA
	P. SCOTT
	D. J. MANNING
West Clare Creameries Ltd	P.F. MAGUIRE
	T. PRENDEVILLE
Junior	SEAN DOYLE
Travelling Creameries	J. MOYNIHAN

CORK

Bandon CDS Ltd	W. WALL
Ballyclough CDS Ltd	J. J. MYERS
	C.J. POWER
	M. WALSH
Barryroe CDS Ltd	M. McCARTHY
Boherbue CA &DS Ltd	P. BREEN

Castlelyons CDS Ltd	P. HEALY
	G. FRANKLIN
Castletownbere Creamery	M.J. O'LEARY
Travelling Creameries	D. CROWLEY
	J.B. FITZGERALD
	J.J. MURPHY
Clondrohid CDS Ltd	T.S. RIORDAN
Coachford Creamery	T.A. STACK
	P. CURRAN
Drinagh CDS Ltd	J. BEECHINOR
	D. O'SHEA (A/cs)
	T. McCARTHY
Dromtariffe CDS Ltd	M. O'HANLON
Junior	D. O'CONNOR
Freemount DS Ltd	J.J. MORAN
Kilcorney CDS Ltd	J. CREEDON
Killumney CDS Ltd	H. CREEDON
Lisavard CDS Ltd	T.P. KINGSTOWN
	J. O'DONOVAN
	J. SHORTEN
Milford CDS Ltd	T.P. STRITCH
	T. STOKES
Mitchelstown CC Ltd	W.D. HAYES
	J. McCARTHY, BSc
	T. NEVILLE, BSc
	Wm. CASEY
	M. ELLARD
	W. O'NEILL
	T. RYAN
	F.P. ROCHE
	P. DOWLING BSc
	E. MAGNER BSc
	J.A. QUISH
Muskerry & Lissarda CC Ltd	PATK KENNEALLY
Newmarket CDS Ltd	DENIS RYAN
Junior	D.D. MURPHY
North Cork CDS Ltd	J. MURPHY
Shandrum Co-op Creamery	C. HAWE
	M. RYAN
Terelton Creamery	P. DWYER
	D. TANGNEY
Travelling Creamery	J.C. FLYNN
University College Cork	J.J. MURPHY, B. Com
West Cork Creameries	M. WALSH

Junior	H. O'NEILL
Travelling Creameries	P.O'MAHONY
	P. GRIFFIN
	J. O'DONOGHUE

KERRY
Abbeydorney CDS Ltd	vacant
Ardfert Creamery	P. E. O'DRISCOLL
Junior	M. DOWLING
Cahirciveen Creamery	J.P. ENRIGHT
Junior	P. MURPHY
Travelling Creameries	J.O'SULLIVAN
	G.O'SULLIVAN
	R. KISSANE
	F. O'NEILL, BSc
Castlemaine Creamery	D. K. MULLINS
	T. MANGAN
Travelling Creameries	T. O'SULLIVAN
	H. SPRING
	B. DALY
Dicksgrove Creamery	D. TOBIN
	M. McCARTHY
Travelling Creamery	Wm. PRENDEVILLE
Dingle Creamery	S.P. O'LAOGHAIRE
	T. O'FLAHERTY
Kenmare Creamery	T. O'BRIEN
Travelling Creameries	T. O'HANLON
	J. POWER
	T.CONDON BSc
	J. McCARTHY
Lee Strand CDS Ltd	T. COSTELLOE
Listowel Creamery	P.J. RYAN
	T. FLYNN
	K. LEAHY
Travelling Creamery	W. HARTNETT
Lixnaw Creamery	J. CONWAY
Newtownsandes CDS Ltd	M. MULVIHILL
Rathmore Creamery	P.J. RYAN
	P. DALY
Travelling Creameries	S. MURPHY
	P. O'REILLY

KILKENNY

Barrowvale CC Ltd	P. J. O'DONOHOE
Callen CDS Ltd	P. SCRIVEN
	J. FITZPATRICK
Freshford CDS Ltd	Vacant
Glenmore CDS Ltd	K. CUDDIHY
	W. CAHILL
Kilkenny CDS Ltd	S. LANDERS
Kilmanagh CDS Ltd	W. WALSH
Windgap CDS Ltd	J. PRENDERGAST

LEITRIM

Killasnett CDS Ltd	J.P. DRUMM
Kiltoghert CDS Ltd	D. McDERMOTT

LIMERICK

Abington CDS Ltd	W. O'ROURKE
Annacotty CDS Ltd	J. MOYNIHAN
Ardagh CDS Ltd	W. O'CONNELL
Askeaton CDS Ltd	D.J. O'RIORDAN
Athea CDS Ltd	W. J. HURLEY
Ballyagran CDS Ltd	L.E. CARR
Belville Deal Bridge CDS	T. KEANE
Blackabbey CDS Ltd	P. MARRON
Cahirconlish CDS Ltd	J. O'CONNOR
Cappamore CS & DS Ltd	S. CRONIN
Castlemahon CDS Ltd	W. P. HEFFERNAN
Clouncagh CDS Ltd	E. BAGGOTT
C.M. Co. Ltd Lansdowne	P. HICKEY
	P. J. JACOB BSc
	J. MURPHY
C.M. Co. Ltd Knocklong	J. O'DOHERTY, BSc
	E. O'DWYER
Junior	B. McGONIGLE, BSc
Devon Road CDS Ltd	P. DEE
Drombanna CDS Ltd	T. NORMOYLE
	M. O'FARRELL, BSc
Dromkeen CDS Ltd	B. HOWARD
Effin CDS Ltd	O. O'BRIEN
	P.J. LACEY
Feenagh CDS Ltd	D.F. LEAHY
Garryspillane CDS Ltd	R. STAPLETON

217

Glenwilliam CDS Ltd	T. FINN
Greybridge CDS Ltd	J. F. HASTINGS
Herbertstown CDS Ltd	PATK. REARDON
Hospital CDS	M. MARTIN
Kantoher CDS Ltd	M. J. O'CONNOR
	J. DORE
Kildimo	S. RYAN
Kilfinny CDS Ltd	P.C. BURKE
	D. KEATING BSc
Kilmallock CDS Ltd	J. HOULIHAN
Mount Collins CDS Ltd	D. O'SULLIVAN
	J. O'CONNELL
Oola CDS Ltd	R. HEWSTON
Rathkeale CDS Ltd	J. O'RIORDAN
Sarsfield CDS Ltd	M. O'DWYER
Shanagolden CDS Ltd	M. O'SHAUGHNESSY
	J. QUINN
Toher CDS Ltd	J. ALLIS
Tournafulla CDS Ltd	P. ROCHE
	JOHN J. CURTIN
	S. RYAN

MONAGHAN

Lough Egish CDS Ltd	M. O'LEARY
Town of Monaghan CDS Ltd	P.J. CAHILL

SLIGO

Achonry CDS Ltd	C.FINAN
Ballinfull CDS Ltd	M. McLEAN
Ballintrillick CDS Ltd	D. McGOWAN
Drumcliffe CDS Ltd	W. MEEHAN
Riverstown CA & DS Ltd	J. CONLON

TIPPERERY

Ballingarry CDS Ltd	JAMES DUNNE
Boherlahan CDS Ltd	T. JOYE
Borrisoleigh CDS Ltd	T. RYAN (Jr)
Centenary CDS Ltd	W. KENNEDY
Clonmel and Newcastle CC	B. O'KEEFFE
	W.F. MORRISSEY
Coolmoyne and Fethard CDS	J. LUCEY

Drombane CDS Ltd	T. COOKE
Fennor CA & DS Ltd	D. CASEY
Hollyford CA & DS Ltd	J. RYAN
Kilross CDS Ltd	J.O'CONNELL
Knockavardagh CDS Ltd	P.L. HORGAN
Nenagh CDS Ltd	J.P. QUILL
Newport CDS Ltd	M. BARRY
Outrath CDS Ltd	D. LYONS
	T. CURRAN
Solohead CDS Ltd	J. O'DWYER
Suirvale CDS Ltd	J. ENNIS
	P. BUTLER
Thurles CDS Ltd	P. QUINLAN
Tipperary CC Ltd	F. J. DALY
	M.J. CASEY
Tipperary C. M. Co. Ltd	M. FITZGERALD
	M. O'CONNELL, BSc
Junior	G.SUGRUE
	B. CAHILL

WEXFORD

Inch CDS Ltd	J. O'MAHONY

WATERFORD

Dungarvan CDS Ltd	P. NEVILLE
	W. WALSH
Junior	S. O'CONNOR
	T. McGRATH
Knockmeal CDS Ltd	J.J O'KEEFFE
	E. DUNNE
Kilmeaden CC LTD	T. MURPHY, BSc
	J. MURRAY

NUMBER OF
CENTRAL AND AUXILIARY CREAMERIES
IN IRELAND 1956

	CENTRALS	AUXILIARIES
ARMAGH		1
ANTRIM	5	2
CARLOW		1
CAVAN	4	24
CLARE	4	33
CORK	25	121
DERRY	1	-
DONEGAL	2	8
DOWN	1	-
FERMANAGH	5	-
KERRY	15	46
KILKENNY	21	15
LEIITRIM	2	14
	CENTRALS	**AUXILIARIES**
LEIX	1	2
LIMERICK	42	47
LONGFORD		2
MEATH		1
MONAGHAN	3	17
ROSCOMMON	1	4
SLIGO	8	12
TIPPERRY	25	68
TYRONE	3	2
WATERFORD	5	19
WEXFORD	1	2
TOTALS	174	440

HEADQUARTERS ADDRESSES
OF DAIRY PRODUCE INSPECTORS
1956
EIRE

CHIEF DAIRY PRODUCE INSPECTOR

Dr A.J. Hennerty, Room 137, Department of Agriculture, Dublin.

SENIOR DAIRY PRODUCE INSPECTORS

Mr P. Power	West St., Callan , Co. Kilkenny.
Mr M. Pierce	Broadford, Charleville, Co. Cork.
Mr R. Hannigan	19 Chapel St., Sligo, Co. Sligo.
Mr C.J. McCarthy	Room 137, Dept. of Agriculture.

JUNIOR INSPECTORS

Mr J. P. Buckley	'Dromore' Upper Beaumont | Drive, Ballintemple, Cork.
Mr H. M. Byrne	Upper Lewis Road, Killarney, Co. Kerry.
Mr C. Cregan	Bohercrowe, Tipperary.
Mr J. Curtin	16 Bridge St., Listowel, Co Kerry
Mr P. Curtin	'Hillsboro,' Ashbourne Avenue, Limerick.
Mr M. A. Keaney	2 Highland Terrace, Carrick-on-Shannon, Co. Leitrim.
Mr W. P. McLoughlin	Mill Street House, Monaghan.
Mr P.J. Carroll	Farnam Hotel, Cavan.
Mr T.C. Murray	Cabra Road, Thurles, Co. Tipperary.
Mr H. S. O'Connell	Quay Street, Donegal.
Mr J. O'Connor	Sunville, Newmarket, Co. Cork.
Mr C. O'Connor	'Harrowville', Dublin Road, Kilkenny.
Mr Wm. O'Connor	'Ayle', Mail Coach Road, Sligo.
Mr. D. Dempsey	Walker's Row, Fermoy, Co. Cork.
Mr M. O'Doherty	Cappa, Kilrush, Co. Clare.
Mr. P. J. O'Donovan	10 The Square, Clonakilty, Co. Cork.
Mr P. O'Keeffe	Marino Terrace, Bantry , Co Cork.
Mr S. O'Ruairc	Churchtown, Newcastlewest, Co. Limerick.
Mr C. Quaid	Ardyoul, Kilmallock, Co Limerick.
Mr P. Shine	38 Lowertown, Waterford.
Mr W. Wallace	Bungalow, Fethard, Co. Tipperary.

Appendix 1
The Dairy Disopsal Company

Dairy Disposal Company Ltd, Head Office; 5 South Frederick Street, Dublin.

Directors; John Hennigan (chairman), T. Dennehy , Ch Fletcher, Patk. McDermott, Martin J. Mullally, Thomas O'Sullivan.

The extent of creameries owned and operated by the Dairy Disposal Company Ltd in 1956

Central: North Clare, Ennistymon

Branches:

Ballinacarra, Kilfenora	Kilminchey , Ennis
Coore, Miltown-Malbay	Kilnamona, Ennis
Darragh, Ennis	Liscannor, Lachinch
Honan's Bridge, Miltown	Moy, Lahinch
Inagh, Ennis	Smithstown, Kilshanny

Seven Travelling Creameries.
1 Noughaval, Toovahera, Carron, Leitra
2. Crusheen, Barefield, Ruan, Kells
3. Crawfords Shop, Fermoyle, Kanturk, Lisroe
4. Caherconnell, Ballyvaughan, Fanore, Ballinalacken.
5. Corofin, Kilnaboy, Kahaska, Inch.
6. Talty's Cross, Fitzpatricks Cross Bartra, Moymore.,
7. Furaglin, Wilbrook, Drinagh, Dysart

Central: East Clare, Scariff

Branches;
Feakle,
Tulla
Whitegate
Four Travelling Creameries

Central: West Clare, Kilrush

Branches

Annageragh, Mullagh
Bella Cross , Carrigaholt
Blackweir, Lisdean
Clondegad, Ballynacally
Cooraclone, Cranny
Cranny.
Doonaha,, Kilkee

Kildysert, Ennis
Kilmihill.
;Kilmurray McMahon
Labasheeba, Kilrush
Powers Cross, Doonbeg
Derrylough, Killimer
Kilbaha, Kilkee

Two travelling creameries

Central: Castletownbere Creamery Company

Branches
Bere Island
Three Travelling Creameries.

Central: Coachford Creamery (Newmarket Dairy Co)

Branches

Berrings,
Killerdish
Kilcoleman
Macroom
Killinardrish

Caum
Dripsey
Coachford
Rusheen
Rylane

Central: Terelton (NDC)

Branches

Ballingeary
Bengour
Mossgrove
Inchageela
Teergay
Togher

Killowen
Enniskeen
Mount Pleasant
Shinaugh
Toames

One Travelling Creamery

Central: West Cork Creameries, Aghadown (DDC)

Branches
Churchcross	Dreenybridge
Gurteenakilla	Ballydehob
Kilcoe	Skeagh

Whiddy Island. (The shed beyond the pub was where the creamery branch was told to the author by a Bantry man who delivered milk as a boy).
Three Travelling Creameries

Central: (Kerry), Ardfert (DDC)

Branches
Ballyheigue	Ballymacquinn
Abedorney	Banemore
Causeway	Chapletown

Central: Caherciveen

Branches
Ballinskelligs	Ceim
Valentia	

Four Travelling Creameries

Central: Dicksgrove (DDC)

Branches
Ballymacelligott	Cordae
Gortalea	Kilcummin
Scartaglen	Tobarmaig.

One Travelling creamery

Central: Dingle (DDC)

Branches

Annascaul

Feonagh

Castlegregory

Lispole

Ventry

Ballyferriter

Camp

Cloghhere

Stradbally

Central: Kenmare (DDC)

Four Travelling Creameries

Central: (DDC) Listowel

Branches

Ballylongford

Kilcoleman

Lisselton

Tarbert

One Travelling Creamery

Cooladerrig

Kilmorna

Lyreacompane

Central: Rathmore (DDC)

Branches

Ballydaly

Anabla

Bealnadeega

Clohare

Two Travelling Creameries

Millstreet

Lacka

St. Brendans

Gullane

34 travelling Creameries in all

Central: Condensed Milk Company of Ireland, Lansdowne, Limerick

Branch
  Dromkeen

Central: Knocklong

Branches
  Ballinveena
  Bulgaden
  Gormanstown
  Milltown

  Ballylanders
  Elton
  Knocklong

Central: Tipperary

Branches
  Annacarty
  Bansha
  Clogher
  Grange
  Greenane
  Rossmore

  Ballybrack
  Blackbridge
  Glenough
  Grantstown
  Kilmoyle

Appendix 2
Irish Creamery Managers' Association
now known as the
Dairy Executives Association

The Irish Creamery Managers Association

The Irish Creamery Managers Association was founded in 1899 to represent Creamery Managers in various matters. And issued its own exam based Certification in 1914 based on the 3x20 week course. By the end of 1904, the ICMA had matured with the objects of the association being:-
- To obtain and disseminate to its members all information on dairying and all matters likely to affect the interests of the Managers of Creameries
- To improve the status of the Managers by promoting technical instruction and training in the general business of management of creameries and to afford facilities for such instruction to Managers at present employed.
- To provide Sickness and Accident Benefits and other allowances to members in circumstances where such allowances appear to be justifiable.
- And later to assist the Creamery managers in any personal or collective situations they found themselves with their employers

At this time, the ICMA had members in all four provinces, including what late became the six counties.

From 1906 it produced a monthly journal called the Creamery Manager and a yearly Yearbook and Dairy. In 1920 the Journal was renamed the Irish Agricultural and Creamery Review

The first general Secretary was D. Hegarty, 5 South Mall Cork. At this time the Association had some 700 members.

In the 1920s, the ICMA purchased premises at 32 Kildare Street, Dublin subsequently moving to 33 Kildare Street where it in to this day, virtually across the road from Leinster House. The longest serving General Secretary of the ICMA was Captain D.J. Barry who served from the 1920's until the 1970's and was as well known in the industry as Irish Whisky. A tireless worker he served on the first Board of the Irish Dairy Board and was well respected as a negotiator in securing the best deals possible for his members.

Following D.J. Barry was Mr M.V. Murtagh, and the current General Secretary In Mr Sean Lane who, through his hard work has brought the Dairy Executives Association to record membership – like he did with Dublin!

CERTIFICATES
Revised Scheme.
The Central Council of the Irish Creamery Managers' Association are now prepared to grant certificates of proficiency on the following conditions:-

EXISTING MANAGERS
1. The Central Council will grant Certificates of Proficiency to existing managers who apply for same provided they satisfy the Council that they have sufficient knowledge of Accontancy, Business methods, Dairy Technology, Dairy Bacteriology and Dairy Engineering.

2. The proficiency of each candidate in the subjects named may be decided partly by his record and partly by examination. A candidate who has managed a Central Creamery for not less than nine years or who has managed a Central Creamery for six years , preceded or followed by a period of not less than five years as assistant manager or manager of an auxiliary, may, however be exempted by the Central Council from the examination.

3. No manager, irrespective of service shall receive a certificate who is known to be incompetent to fill the position which he holds at the time, or whose character in business or business habits are not satisfactory.

4. A certificate once issued can only be withdrawn from a member by a vote of three-fourths of the members present at a meeting of the Central Council in respect of which the notice of the proposed withdrawal is contained in the notice convening the meeting, the Council need not assign any reason for withdrawal of a certificate.

5. At least once in the year the Council shall publish a list of persons to whom the certificate of the Association has been awarded, and distribute copies free of charge to all creamery owners.

6. Subject to the provisions provided in paragraph 7, each candidate required to undergo the examinations must, to qualify for the certificate, obtain not less than 60 per cent of the maximum marks laid down for each subject.

7. A candidate for the certificate who undergoes the examination and who :-
(a) Has acted not less than four years as manager of a Central Creamery ;or who
(b) Has acted not less than three years as manager of a Central Creamery, preceded or followed by a period of not less that three years as assistant manager or manager of an auxiliary or who
(c) Has acted not less than six years as assistant manager or manager of and auxiliary.

Will be allowed experience marks for each subject of the examination as per paragraph eight and if such experience marks, when added to the marks awarded for answering at the examination, make the total not less than 60% of the maximum obtainable, he will be entitled to the certificate in the same manner as if the total of not less than 60%, were awarded solely for answering at the examination.

8. The experience marks provided in paragraph seven shall be awarded as follows:-
(a) For each year of service over and above three years as manager of a Central Creamery – 5%
(b) For each year of service over and above three years as assistant manager or manager of an Auxiliary – 21/2 %
Provided that the total experience marks awarded shall in no case exceed 30% of the maximum for each subject

9. the Certificate shall be in the following form
THIS CERTIFICATE is awarded to Mr.......of.........who has satisfied th Central Council of the Irish Creamery Managers Association that he is qualified to act as manager of a Central Creamery
Signed on behalf of the Central Council
        President
        Vice-President
        Secretary.

10. The Central Council shall have power to alter, amend or supplement these Rules from time to time as they may consider desirable, but due notice of and material alteration or addition shall be given to the members. They may also, without assigning any reason, refuse to admit a candidate for examination , or refuse to grant a certificate to any particular candidate or dispute, or any matter not provided for in these Rules.

11. CERTIFICATES TO NON-MANAGERS Persons who have not actually managed a creamery or auxiliary may be admitted to the examination referred to in the preceding paragraphs provided they have spent a term of not less than five months in a dairy school at which the management of creameries is specially taught, and served not less than ten months as a pupil or apprentice at an approved creamery or creameries.

12. The examination ,which will be conducted by a Board of Examiners appointed by the Central Council, will, as far as possible, be confined to the syllabus appended to these rules, but the Central council will not require the Examiners to adhere strictly to same.

13. Applications for admission to the examinations must be in the form provided by the Council for that purpose and each must be accompanied by a fee of Ten

Shillings. The Candidate will get due notice of the centre or centres at which the Examination will be held (A copy of the Syllabus can be had on application to the Central Secretary)

Examinations for ICMA Certificate were held at Limerick, Waterford, Enniskillen and Omagh, on March 9th and 10th 1915. The questions of the written portion of the examination are given below.
The Examiners were as follows;-

Dairy Technology-
    Jn. Wm. Tayleur, BSc (Lond). NDD
    James Fant, Chief Dairy Expert IAOS

Dairy Engineering-
    James Fant, Chief Dairy Expert IAOS
    William Frazer, 1st Cl. B. of T. Certificate

Accountancy & Business Methods
    J. H. Barton. of Messrs. Cooper & Kennys, Public Auditors, Dublin.
    D. Hegarty, ICMA

The oral examination at the different centres was conducted by Messrs, Tayleur, Fant, and Hegarty. Subsequently all the Examiners held a meeting in Dublin, for the purpose of awarding marks to the candidates' worked papers. The results will be published later.

CERTIFICATE IN CREAMERY MANAGEMENT
EXAMINATION – MARCH 1915
DAIRY TECHNOLOGY

Time – Two and a half hours (10 a.m. to 12.30 p.m.
(Not more than 10 questions to be attempted)
Write your own Register number (but not your name) at the head of each sheet.

1. State the foods (obtainable by ordinary farmers) for dairy cows for summer and winter feeding that you consider will secure the best results. What foods are unsuitable for dairy cows? Give briefly reasons for your replies.

2. What are the principal constituent and the percentages of same in average whole milk freshly drawn from a cow?

3. What are the principal sources of contamination of milk supplies before they

reach the creameries, and what effect have temperatures on the keeping qualities of milk supplies for creameries?

4. Why do you heat the whole milk before separating it, and what effect has the heating on the process of separation? What circumstances guide you in regulating the separating temperature?

5. How would you determine the acidity in a sample of cream, and what re-agents would you use?

6. Describe the most reliable and practical method that you know of for preparing and propagating a pure starter in a creamery. What utensils, materials and temperatures would you use?

7. What acidity, churning temperatures, and general methods would you adopt in the manufacture of first-class creamery butter, and how does acidity and temperature affect the yield and quality of the butter?

8. What are the chief commercial characteristics that largely determine the quality and value of creamery butter, and state how they must be secured?

9. If you suspected the purity of the water supply what local and other steps would you take to test its effects on the quality of the butter?

10. Describe a good method of preparing cream for sale, and what are the chief commercial properties it should possess? What equipment is desirable to secure them?

11. Indicate how you would determine the nett price f.o.b. per cwt. for butter that would be equal to selling cream containing 50 per cent. Butterfat at 7s. per gallon free on rail in purchasers cans?

12. Describe the best method you can adopt foe determining the percentage of fat in milk and cream at a creamery. What chemicals would you use, and what is the effect of each for testing purposes?

13. What are the principal causes of poor yield (or 'produce') in a creamery? What steps would you take to trace the causes, and what remedies would you apply to prevent its continuance?

14. If you were manager of a small Creamery whose milk supply was very limited, but which had four small separate or independent auxiliaries supplying it with cream, what practical methods would you adopt to produce one uniform quality of butter and yet credit each creamery with its just yield of butter?

DAIRY ENGINEERING
Time – one and a half hours (12.30 to 2pm)
(Not more than 5 questions to be attempted)
Write your Register number (but not your name) at the head of each sheet.

1. Explain how you would set about the starting of a steam engine, describing the various steps in detail, and giving your reasons for each?

2. A knock is heard from an engine at work. To what might this be due, and state fully how you would proceed to locate and remedy it?

3. Assuming that you have a boiler under your control how would you proceed , first on arrival in the morning, and before getting up steam, second, while getting up steam; third, during the day: forth ,what should be done before leaving at night?

4. Assuming that a boiler under your control became short of water while at work, state fully how you would proceed, and give your reasons?

5. What are your ideas regarding the essential qualities of good coal for boiler purposes? What in your opinion would be the causes of a boiler giving off large quantities of black smoke, and what steps would you take to effect a remedy.

6. An engine set to run at 175 revolutions per minute has a driving pulley of 36 inches in diameter, what diameter pulley would be required for the shafting to run the latter at 150 revolutions per minute?

7. What is the principle on which a separator removes the cream from the milk? Name the principal factors that are possible in a creamery to interfere with the efficiency of a separator, and how would you guard against them?

8. If the capacity of the water pump decreased while there was still sufficient water in the well, what would be the probable causes, and how would you set about rectifying them?

9. What do you consider are the advantages of a modern combined churn over the types of churn in use some ten years ago? Give your reasons for the advantages which you consider the combined churn possesses.

ACCOUNTANCY AND BUSINESS METHODS

Time – Two and a half hours (3 pm to 5.30).
(Not more than 5 questions in Section 1 and 5 in Section 2 are to be attempted).
Write your Register Number (but not your name) at the top of each sheet.
Section 1

1. What account books are essential in a Central Creamery? State briefly the object of each.

2. How would you satisfy yourself that the full quantity of butter manufactured (and purchased, if any) had been properly accounted for in the books, and in what way may leakages be immediately detected?

3. State your method of verifying the bank balance according to the Cash Book at the end of each month, with that shown by the Bank Pass Book.

4. To what accounts in the Impersonal Ledger should the following purchases by charged?
    (a) New Engine
    (b) Sheet Iron Chimney ,for boiler
    (c) Belting
    (d) Separator Bowl
    (e) Cream Vat
    (f) Boiler/ Tubes
    (g) Piston Rods
Give reason for answer in each case.

5. Explain briefly principles of Double Entry Book-keeping, and what are its advantages over Single Entry system.

6. On 1st March, 1914, you accept from a customer a promissory note for £10, payable in one month, in settlement of his account. The Customer fails to meet the note on maturity, and you are required to explain what entries are necessary to record the transaction. It is presumed the promissory note was lodged in the Bank on 1st March, 1914.

7. From the following Trial Balance prepare a Trading Account, Profit and Loss Account and Balance Sheet of the Ballyhooley o-operative Association Society, Ltd,. for the year ended 31st December , 1914

	£ s d	£ s d
Milk Purchases	8,000 0 0	
Butter Sales		9,000 0 0
Salaries & Wages	200 0 0	
Packages &		

233

Parchment	50 0 0	
Oil & Waste	10 0 0	
Repairs	20 0 0	
Salt & preservative	18 0 0	
Coal	40 0 0	
Rents, Rates, Taxes & Insurance	30 0 0	
Postage & Teleg	15 0 0	
Stationery & Print	10 0 0	
Interest On Bank Overdraft	8 0 0	
Cheque books	10 0 0	
Sundry Expenses	5 0 0	
Carriage & Cartage	80 0 0	
Stock on hands; 1st Jon., 1914	50 0 0	
Profit & Loss A/c Balance 1st Jan. 1914		845 0 0
Machinery do.	1,500 0 0	
Buildings do.	800 0 0	
Share Capital do.		1,000 0 0
Sundry Trade Cr 31st Dec. 1914	300 0 0	
Sundry Debtors do	500 0 0	
Cash on Hands do	5 0 0	
Balance due to Bank 31st December 1914		206 0 0
	£11,351 0 0	£11,351 0 0

The Stock on hands on 31st December, 1914, was £40 0s 0d. Write Depreciation off Machinery, and Buildings at the rate of 10% and 5% respectively.

SECTION 2

8. (a) What are the essential points in a 'Contract' or 'Sale

(b) The following telegrams have passed between a butter merchant and a creamery;-

FROM MERCHANT TO CREAMERY.- 'Offer you One hundred and eight for forty boxes of butter, rail to-morrow. Wire acceptance immediately'

FROM CREAMERY TO MERCHANT.- 'Accept hundred and eight but cannot forward to-morrow. Will forward in four days unless we hear from you to the contrary'

The Merchant sends no reply. The creamery forwards the butter four days later and it is refused by the merchant, though it has reached him in good condition. Can the creamery recover the whole or any portion of the invoiced price (108s).? Give reasons for your reply.
(c) If offering the same lot of butter to two or more buyers simultaneously, give the words of the telegram you would despatch to each.

9. James Thompson, Limited, write complaining that 40 boxes of butter purchased from your creamery at 111s per cwt. nett f.o.r. have been delayed in transit, causing a loss of 10s. per cwt., allowance of £10.
Write a letter in reply.

10. Draft a Price List form in the manner in which you would hand it to your printers for the production of copies sufficient to last the whole season. Include the instructions you would give to the printers.

11. Before giving credit what are the principal points on which you should satisfy yourself if the prospective buyer were : (a) a company, (b) a firm, (c) an individual.

12. (a) By what route would you forward goods to Newcastle on Tyne from any town(to be named) in your own county? Give the names of the carrying companies which would be concerned.
(b) State what you know about 'Owner's Risk' and 'company risk rates also 'through' rates.

13. If opening a newly erected Creamery to deal with an annual turnover of £10,000 what fittings, stationery, etc would you order for the office? (you need not include account books)

14 Write (using fictitious names) what you consider would be the minutes of the proceedings of the first monthly meeting of the committee of Management of a newly established Co-operative Creamery Society? Assume that the creamery has been receiving milk and manufacturing butter for the month previous to the date of the meeting.

Followed by the First Year apprenticeship in a Central Creamery. When the Department of Agriculture and Technical Instruction was set up in 1901

SELECT BIBLIOGRAPHY

At the Sign of the Cow, Colin Rynne, Collins Press, 1998.

The Irish Co-operative Movement, Patrick Bolger, Institute of Public Administration, 1977.

The Creamery Manager - Journal of the Irish Creamery Managers Association, 1914 Yearbook.

Remembering the Creameries, Maura Cronin, Ireland's Heritage, Ashgate, 2005.

Journal of the Society of Dairy Technology, 'The Irish Dairy Industry; a historical perspective,' John Foley, Vol. 46, No. 4, November 1993.

Dáil Éireann, Parliamentary Debates, Vol. 89, 24 March 1943.

'History of the Development of the Irish Cheese Industry,' John McCarthy, 3rd Cheese Symposium, National Dairy Products Research Centre, Moorepark, October 1992.

Mitchelstown Through Seven Centuries, Bill Power, Mount Cashell Books, 1996.

Images of Mitchelstown, Bill Power, Mount Cashell Books, 2002.

From the Danes to Dairygold, Bill Power, Mount Cashell Books, 1996.

The Creamery Manager - Journal of the Irish Creamery Managers Association, 1914 Yearbook.

University College Cork Sessional Lists, Cork University Press, 1927-28.

University College Cork Sessional Lists, Cork University Press, 1928-29.

University College Cork Sessional Lists, Cork University Press, 1929-30.

Creamery Yearbook and Dairy, 1956, 1959, Irish Creamery Managers' Association.

Commercial Methods of Testing Milk and Milk Products, J. Lyons, M.J. O'Shea, Cork University Press.

Ballyclough Co-operative Creamery Ltd, A History, 1908-1990, John Hough, 2008.

Dáil Éireann Parliamentary Debates, 13th November 1992.

Hughes News, Staff magazine of Hughes Brothers Ltd, Hazelbrook Dairy, Rathfarnham, Dublin December 1965

Dairying – A Modern Industry with Roots in Pre-history, National Dairy Council 1982.

The Department's Story, by Daniel Hoctor. IPA 1971.

The First Department, History of Department of Agriculture, Mary E. Daly 2002.

Fruits of a Century - Illustrated History of the IAOS/ ICOS 1894-1994, I.C.O.S.